Level K

From Phonics to Reading

Wiley Blevins

Sadlier School

Douglas Fisher, Ph.D.

Senior Series Reviewer
Professor of Education
San Diego State University
San Diego, CA

Reviewers

The publisher wishes to thank for their comments and suggestions the following teachers
and administrators, who read portions of the series prior to publication.

Mindy Jo Acton
Third Grade Teacher
Barnesville Elementary
Barnesville, OH

Kathy W. Dames, Ed.D.
The Intellectual Child LLC
Flossmoor, IL

Jennifer L. Jones
First Grade Teacher
Resurrection Catholic School
Lakeland, FL

Erin Kent
Remediation Specialist, K-6
Montgomery County Intermediate Unit
Norristown, PA

Nancy Osterreich
Director of Grants and School Improvement
Cicero School District 99
Cicero, IL

Luz Baeza Palomares
General Education Teacher
Discovery Charter School
Chula Vista, CA

Colleen Stahl
Academic Coach
Neshaminy School District
Langhorne, PA

Cover Series Design: Silver Linings Studios; **Cover Illustration:** Russell Benfanti; **Illustration Credits:** Bernard Adnet, Dan Andreasen, Gail Armstrong, Martha Aviles, Constanza Basaluzzo, Tim Bowers, Robin Boyer, Scott Burroughs, Craig Cameron, Mattia Cerato, Elisa Chavarri, Holli Conger, Marcus Cutler, Steliyana Doneva, Nathaniel Eckstrom, Peter Francis, Viviana Garofoli, Alessia Girasole, Olga & Aleksey Ivanov, Katie Kath, Laura Logan, Stephen Lewis, Margeaux Lucas, Tammie Lyon, Benton Mahan, Juan Manuel Moreno, Dan McGeehan, Alejandro O'Kif, Bob Ostrom, Macky Pamintuan, Faith Pray, Kimberly Soderburg, Ken Spengler, Laura Watson.

 is a registered trademark of William H. Sadlier, Inc.

William H. Sadlier, Inc.
9 Pine Street
New York, NY 10005-4700

Printed in the United States of America.
ISBN: 978-1-4217-1540-7
1 2 3 4 5 6 7 8 9 10 WEBC 23 22 21 20 19

Contents

Unit 1: Short *a*

LESSON

1 **Target Skill:** *Mm* **9**
Alphabet: Uppercase Letters   Cumulative Assessment: Lesson 1
Take-Home Book: "My ABC Book"

2 **Target Skill: Short** *a* **21**
Alphabet: Lowercase Letters   Spell and Write
High-Frequency Words: *I, can*   Cumulative Assessment: Lessons 1–2
Take-Home Book: "I Can"

3 **Target Skill:** *Ss* **35**
Alphabet: Uppercase and Lowercase Letters   Spell and Write
High-Frequency Words: *see, a*   Cumulative Assessment: Lessons 1–3
Take-Home Book: "Sam"

4 **Target Skill:** *Tt* **49**
Alphabet: Match Uppercase and   Spell and Write
    Lowercase Letters   Cumulative Assessment: Lessons 1–4
High-Frequency Words: *the, on*
Take-Home Book: "Sam Sat"

5 **Target Skill:** *Pp* **63**
Alphabet: Match Uppercase and   Spell and Write
    Lowercase Letters   Cumulative Assessment: Lessons 1–5
High-Frequency Words: *like, to*
Take-Home Book: "I Like"

Unit 2: Short *i*

LESSON

6   Target Skill: *Nn* **79**

High-Frequency Words: *is, it*   Spell and Write
Take-Home Book: "What Is It?"   Cumulative Assessment: Lessons 1–6

7   Target Skill: Short *i* **91**

High-Frequency Words: *big, little*   Spell and Write
Take-Home Book: "Big and Little"   Cumulative Assessment: Lessons 2–7

8   Target Skill: *Cc* **103**

High-Frequency Words: *my, good*   Spell and Write
Take-Home Book: "Good Cat"   Cumulative Assessment: Lessons 3–8

9   Target Skill: *Ff* **115**

High-Frequency Words: *yes, no*   Spell and Write
Take-Home Book: "Can It Fit?"   Cumulative Assessment: Lessons 4–9

10   Target Skill: *Dd* **127**

High-Frequency Words: *look, he*   Spell and Write
Take-Home Book: "Dan and Dad"   Cumulative Assessment: Lessons 5–10

Unit 3: Short o

LESSON

11   Target Skill: *Hh* **141**

High-Frequency Words: *do, you*   Spell and Write
Take-Home Book: "Hats"   Cumulative Assessment: Lessons 6–11

12   Target Skill: Short *o* **153**

High-Frequency Words: *what, this*   Spell and Write
Take-Home Book: "What Is This?"   Cumulative Assessment: Lessons 7–12

13   Target Skill: *Rr* **165**

High-Frequency Words: *and, under*   Spell and Write
Take-Home Book: "Uh-oh!"   Cumulative Assessment: Lessons 8–13

14   Target Skill: *Bb* **177**

High-Frequency Words: *or, are*   Spell and Write
Take-Home Book: "Good or Bad?"   Cumulative Assessment: Lessons 9–14

15   Target Skill: *Ll* **189**

High-Frequency Words: *up, down*   Spell and Write
Take-Home Book: "Up and Down"   Cumulative Assessment: Lessons 10–15

Unit 4: Short e

LESSON

16 Target Skill: *Kk* 203
High-Frequency Words: *she, her*   Spell and Write
Take-Home Book: "Run, Kim!"   Cumulative Assessment: Lessons 11–16

17 Target Skill: **Short *e*** 215
High-Frequency Words: *make, they*   Spell and Write
Take-Home Book: "Ten Little Men"   Cumulative Assessment: Lessons 12–17

18 Target Skill: *Gg* 227
High-Frequency Words: *where, with*   Spell and Write
Take-Home Book: "Where Am I?"   Cumulative Assessment: Lessons 13–18

19 Target Skill: *Ww* 239
High-Frequency Words: *we, play*   Spell and Write
Take-Home Book: "We Will Win!"   Cumulative Assessment: Lessons 14–19

20 Target Skill: *Xx* 251
High-Frequency Words: *one, have*   Spell and Write
Take-Home Book: "Six Boxes"   Cumulative Assessment: Lessons 15–20

Unit 5: Short u

LESSON

21 Target Skill: *Vv* 265
High-Frequency Words: *go, hurt*   Spell and Write
Take-Home Book: "The Best Vet"   Cumulative Assessment: Lessons 16–21

22 Target Skill: **Short *u*** 277
High-Frequency Words: *day, of*   Spell and Write
Take-Home Book: "The Bus"   Cumulative Assessment: Lessons 17–22

23 Target Skill: *Jj* 289
High-Frequency Words: *said, that*   Spell and Write
Take-Home Book: "What Will Jan Do?"   Cumulative Assessment: Lessons 18–23

24 Target Skill: *Qu* 301
High-Frequency Words: *there, out*   Spell and Write
Take-Home Book: "Quick, Quick, Quick!"   Cumulative Assessment: Lessons 19–24

25 Target Skill: *Yy* 313
High-Frequency Words: *all, read*   Spell and Write
Take-Home Book: "Yes!"   Cumulative Assessment: Lessons 20–25

Unit 6: Introduction to Long Vowels

LESSON

26 Target Skill: Zz **327**

High-Frequency Words: *for, finds*   Spell and Write
Take-Home Book: "Zig, Zag, Buzz!"   Cumulative Assessment: Lessons 21–26

27 Target Skill: Short Vowel Review **339**

High-Frequency Words: *was, too*   Spell and Write
Take-Home Book: "Lots of Fun"   Cumulative Assessment: Lessons 22–27

28 Target Skill: Single Letter Long Vowels *e, i, o* **351**

High-Frequency Words: *come, some*   Spell and Write
Take-Home Book: "We Play"   Cumulative Assessment: Lessons 23–28

29 Target Skill: Final *e* (*a_e*) **363**

High-Frequency Words: *your, very*   Spell and Write
Take-Home Book: "The Hat"   Cumulative Assessment: Lessons 24–29

30 Target Skill: Final *e* (*o_e, i_e*) **375**

High-Frequency Words: *use, blue*   Spell and Write
Take-Home Book: "The Bike Ride"   Cumulative Assessment: Lessons 25–30

Picture, Word, and Letter Cards **387**

Dear Family,

In this unit, your child will learn about words that contain short vowel **a**. He or she will learn the ABCs and to read words with the **short a, m, s, t,** and **p** sounds, such as **am; Sam; at;** and **map**.

Home
Connection

Read Connected Text

For each week's lesson, your child will read a Take-Home Book that focuses on the lesson skill. At week's end, the book will be sent home with your child. Read the book to your child, or read it aloud together, pointing to each word as you say it. Multiple readings will give your child practice with the lesson skill.

Practice with the Take-Home Book

Ask your child to point to words in the story that include the vowel or consonant sound for that lesson.

Have your child tell you about the book in one sentence. Write what your child says and read the description aloud together.

Lesson Skills and Take-Home Books

Lesson 1 **Mm:** "My ABC Book"
Lesson 2 **Short a:** "I Can"
Lesson 3 **Ss:** "Sam"
Lesson 4 **Tt:** "Sam Sat"
Lesson 5 **Pp:** "I Like"

Extend the Learning

With your child, look for words with short vowel **a** in books, signs, magazine covers, etc. Keep a notebook of words you discover.

Challenge your child to identify objects in your home or other locations that have the short vowel **a** sound. For example, "I spy a mat."

 Visit SadlierConnect.com for Student & Family Resources.

Apreciada familia:

En esta unidad, su niño(a) aprenderá palabras que contienen la vocal **a**. Aprenderá el ABC y a leer palabras con el sonido corto de la **a**, y los sonidos de la **m**, de la **s**, de la **t** y de la **p**, tales como **am; Sam; at** y **map**.

Leyendo la historieta en el Take-Home Book

Para cada lección de la semana su niño(a) leerá un cuadernillo de historietas, Take-Home Book, que se enfoca en las destrezas de la lección. Al final de cada semana su niño(a) llevará el cuadernillo a la casa. Lea la historieta a su niño(a) o leánla en voz alta juntos, señalando cada palabra al decirla. Leer varias veces ayudará a su niño(a) a practicar las destrezas de la lección.

Practicando con el Take-Home Book

Pida a su niño(a) señalar en la historieta palabras que incluyan el sonido de la vocal o de la consonante para esa lección. Luego pídale que resuma la historieta en una frase. Escriba lo que dice su niño(a) y después lean juntos lo que escribió.

Lesson Skills and Take-Home Books

Lesson 1 **Mm:** "My ABC Book"
Lesson 2 **Short a:** "I Can"
Lesson 3 **Ss:** "Sam"
Lesson 4 **Tt:** "Sam Sat"
Lesson 5 **Pp:** "I like"

Ampliando el aprendizaje

Con su niño(a) busque palabras con vocales con sonido corto de la **a** en libros, letreros, portadas de revistas, etc. Haga una libreta con palabras que descubran juntos.

Rete a su niño(a) a identificar, ya sea en su casa o en otros lugares, objetos que tengan el sonido corto de la vocal **a**. Por ejemplo: "I spy a mat."

 Visite **SadlierConnect.com** para recursos para el estudiante y la familia.

Uppercase Letters

Directions: Point to the letters as we sing the "Alphabet Song."

A B C D E F G
H I J K L M
N O P Q R S T
U V W X Y Z

Letter Sequence

Directions: Connect the letters in order.

Y •

X •

Z

Start

A •

W •

B •

V •

C •

J • I •

U • K • F •

D •

E •

H • G •

T •

L •

S •

P •

Q •

M •

R •

O •

N •

Name _____

MY ABC Book

1

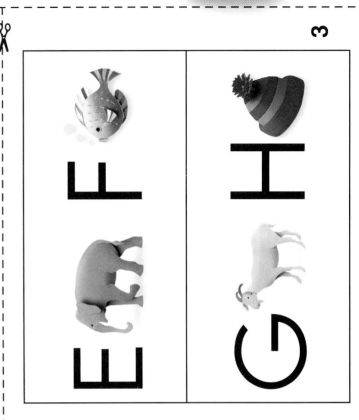

E F

G H

3

Y Z

8

Q R

S T

9

4

K · L
I J

2

A B
C D
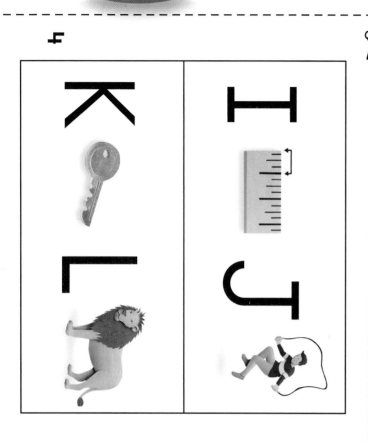

U V
W X

O P
M N
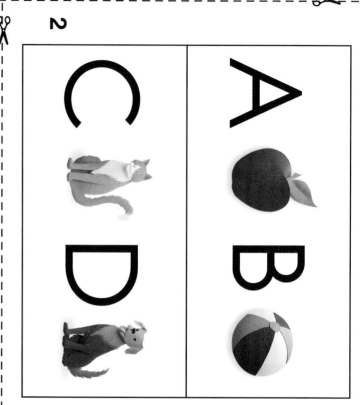

5

7

About Me

Directions: Write your name on the line. Then draw a picture of yourself.

My name is _____.

A Picture of Me

Learn and Say

Directions: Listen and join in.

m...m...m...
Pour the milk in the mug.

Say It

Directions: Say each picture name.
Circle the picture if its name begins with /m/.

1.

2.

3.

4.

5.

6.

Daily Practice

Directions: Do one activity each day. Then check the box.

☐ Sing It Sing the "Alphabet Song" with a partner. Clap when you get to the letter m.

☐ See It Find words in the classroom with the letter m.

Sort It Out

Directions: Look at the pictures on page 387. Say each picture name. Then sort the picture names by beginning sound.

Mm	Not Mm

What words do you know with this sound?

Trace and Write

Directions: Trace and write the letters **M** and **m**. These letters stand for /m/. Say the sound each time you write the letter.

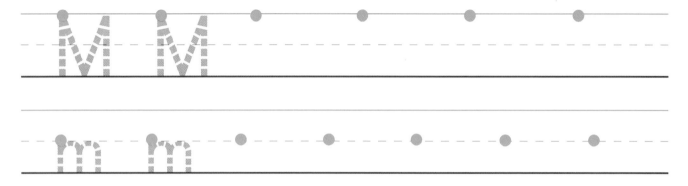

Directions: Say the name of the picture. Write **Mm** on the line if the picture name begins with /m/.

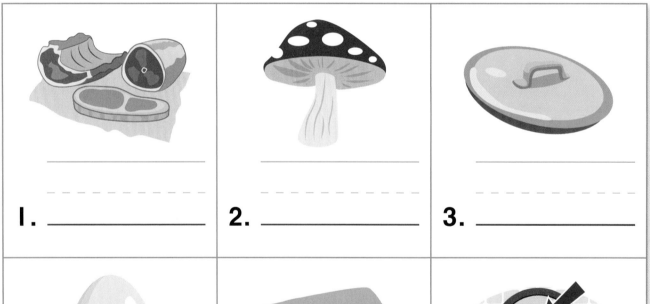

1. _____

2. _____

3. _____

4. _____

5. _____

6. _____

Say and Write

Directions: Say each picture name. Write the letter **m** on the line if the picture name begins with /m/.

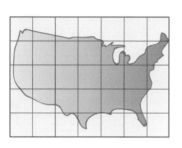

1. _____

2. _____

3. _____

4. _____

5. _____

6. _____

Uppercase Letters

Directions: Color the lily pad to show the letter that comes next.

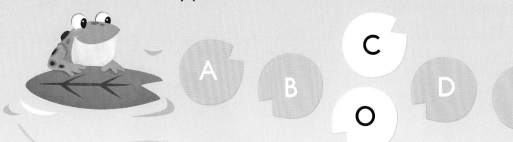

A B C O D E F R

G H K I J X L K

M N O D P Q R B

S F T U V W M X V Y Z

M...m...m...

Directions: Think of a word that begins with /m/.
Tell your teacher a sentence with that word.

Draw About It

Directions: Read "My ABC Book" again.
Write the first letter in your name on the line.
Draw a picture for the letter.

Fluency Check

Directions: Listen to the child read the list below. Mark one check in the green box if the letter-sound is read correctly (accuracy). Mark another check in the blue box if it is read automatically (fluency).

CUMULATIVE ASSESSMENT			
Lesson	**Letter-sound**		
1	m	☐	☐
	a	☐	☐
	b	☐	☐
	s	☐	☐
Number Correct (accuracy): _____ /4			
Number Automatic (fluency): _____ /4			

Lowercase Letters

Directions: Point to the letters as we sing the "Alphabet Song."

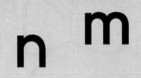

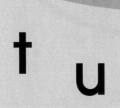

a b c d e f g h i j k l m n o p q r s t u v w x y z

Lowercase Letters

Directions: Connect the letters in order.

Learn and Say

Directions: Listen and join in.

a…a…a…
Bite that apple.

Say It

Directions: Say each picture name.
Circle the picture if its name has the **short** a sound.

1.

2.

3.

4.

5.

6.

Daily Practice

Directions: Do one activity each day. Then check the box.

☐ **Sing It** Sing the "Alphabet Song" with a partner. Clap when you get to the letter a.

☐ **See It** Find words in the classroom with the letter a.

Read-Spell-Write

Directions: Write each word two times. Say each letter as you write it.

I. I _____

2. can _____

Use in Context

Directions: Complete each sentence with a word from above.
Read the finished sentence to a partner.

I. _____ can sit.

2. I _____ hop.

Name _____

I Can

I can run.

I am happy.

2

I can swing.

I can slide.

3

Trace and Write

Directions: Trace and write the letters A and a. These letters stand for the short a sound. Say the sound each time you write the letter.

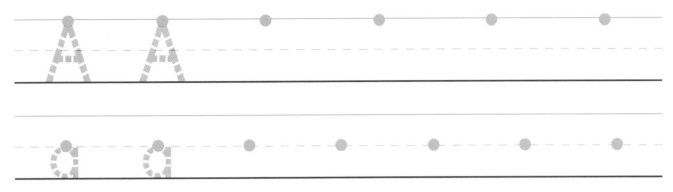

Directions: Say the name of the picture. Write **Aa** on the line if the picture name has the short a sound.

1. _____

2. _____

3. _____

4. _____

5. _____

6. _____

Think and Write

Directions: Say each picture name. Write the letter a if the picture name has the short a sound. Write the letter m if it has the /m/ sound.

1.  _____

2.  _____

3.  _____

4.  _____

5.  _____

6.  _____

Directions: Write your name on the line.

_____

My name is _____.

Trace, Write, and Build

Directions: Trace and write each word.
Then build each word with letter cards.

TRACE	WRITE
I	
can	
am	

Sort It Out

Directions: Look at the pictures on page 387. Say each picture name. Then sort the picture name by vowel sound.

Short a	Not Short a

What words do you know with this sound?

_____

_____

_____

Read and Write

Directions: Say each picture name. Write the letter a if the picture name has the short a sound. Write the letter m if it has the /m/ sound.

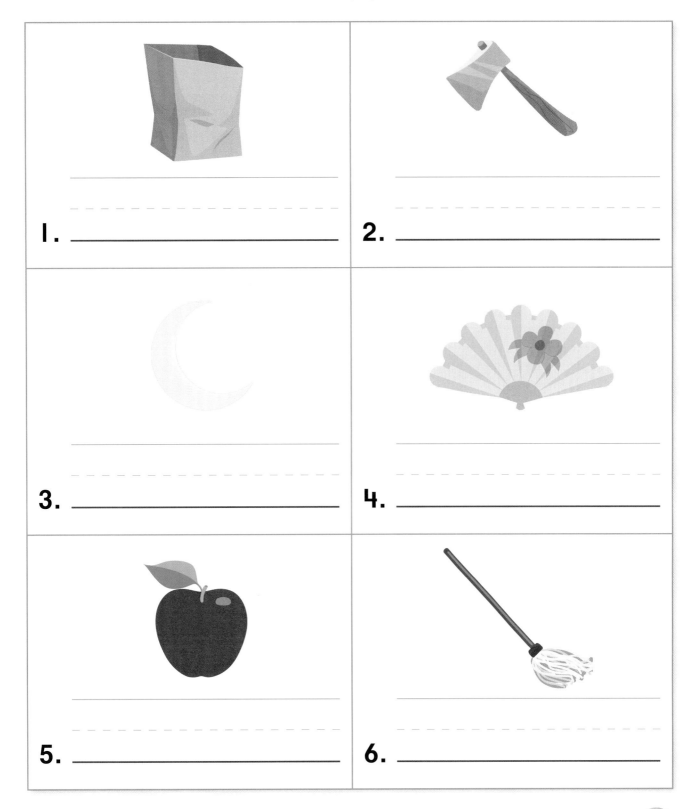

1. _____

2. _____

3. _____

4. _____

5. _____

6. _____

Build Fluency

Directions: Complete each sentence with a word from the box.

I	can

1. I _____ run.

2. Can _____ run?

Directions: Think of a word that has the short a sound. Tell your teacher a sentence with that word.

_____

_____

_____

_____

Draw About It

Directions: Read "I Can" again.
Draw a picture of what the child in the story can do.

Fluency Check

Directions: Listen to the child read the word list. Mark one check in the green box if the word or letter-sound is read correctly (accuracy). Mark another check in the blue box if it is read automatically (fluency).

CUMULATIVE ASSESSMENT			
Lesson	**Letter-sound/Word**		
2	a	☐	☐
	I	☐	☐
	m	☐	☐
	am	☐	☐
1	m	☐	☐
	a	☐	☐
	b	☐	☐
	s	☐	☐

Number Correct (accuracy): _____ /8

Number Automatic (fluency): _____ /8

Fah

Uppercase and Lowercase Letters

Directions: Trace the uppercase and lowercase letters in each line.
Say the letters as you write them.

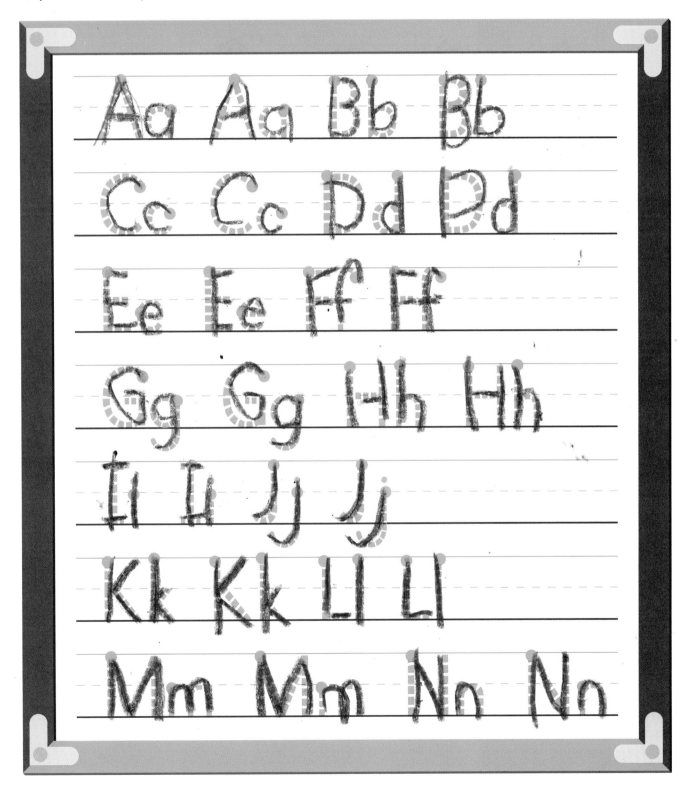

Directions: Trace the uppercase and lowercase letters in each line.
Say the letters as you write them.

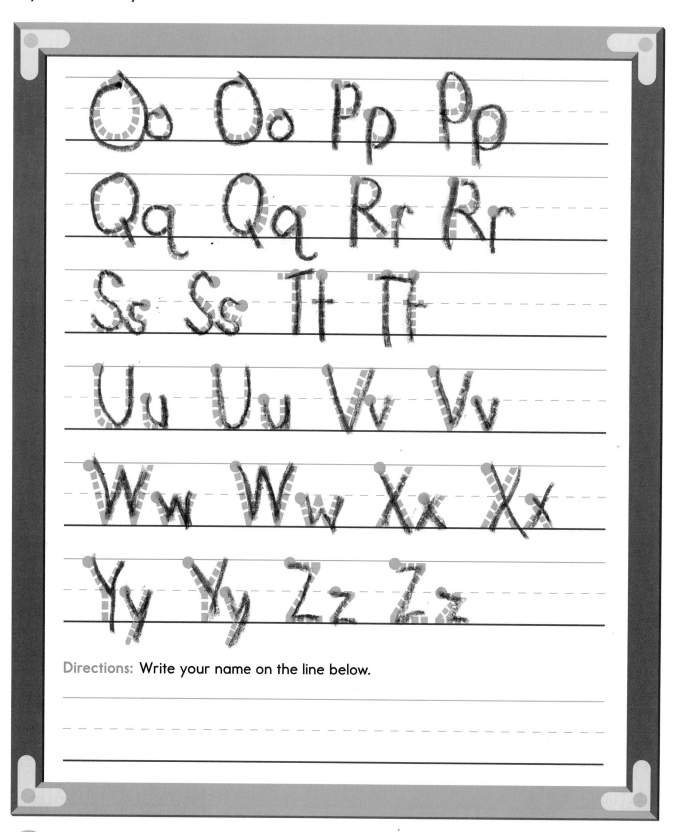

Directions: Write your name on the line below.

Learn and Blend

Directions: Listen and join in.

s...s...s...
Sip soup with a spoon.

Ss

Blend It

Directions: Chorally say the sounds and read the words.

INTRODUCE

1. m   s   a

2. am   Sam

IN CONTEXT

3. I am Sam.

Daily Practice

Directions: Do one activity each day. Then check the box.

☐ **Build Fluency** Read the words each day by yourself and to a partner.

☐ **Mark It** Circle all the words with s.

☐ **Spell It** Sing the "Alphabet Song" with a partner.

☐ **Write About It** Find words in your classroom with s.

Read-Spell-Write

Directions: Write each word two times. Say each letter as you write it.

1. see _See See_

2. a _a a_

Use in Context

Directions: Complete each sentence with a word from above.
Read the finished sentences to a partner.

1. I see _a_ man.

2. I _see_ Sam.

Name _____

Sam

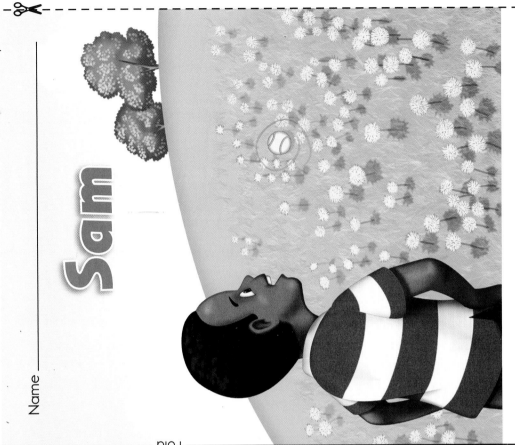

I can see a  .

Fold

I can see Sam.

1

4

2

I can see a .

I can see a  .

3

Trace and Write

Directions: Trace and write the letters **S** and **s**. These letters stand for /s/. Say the sound each time you write the letter.

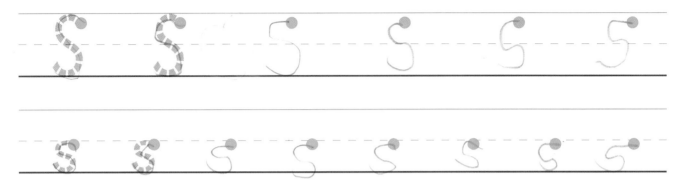

Directions: Say the name of the picture. Write **Ss** on the line if the picture name begins with /s/.

Think and Write

Directions: Listen to each picture name.
Write the first letter of the picture name on the line.

1.  _____

2.  _____

3. **7** _____

4.  _____

Listen and Spell

Directions: Write each word and sentence that you hear.

1. _____

2. _____

Trace, Write, and Build

Directions: Trace and write each word.
Then build each word with letter cards.

TRACE	WRITE
see	
a	
I	
am	
Sam	

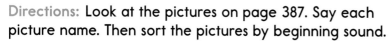

Sort It Out

Directions: Look at the pictures on page 387. Say each picture name. Then sort the pictures by beginning sound.

Ss

Mm

What words do you know with these sounds?

Read and Write

Directions: Say the picture name. Circle the first letter of the picture name.
Write the letter on the line.

a m s **1.** _____	a m s **2.** _____
a m s **3.** _____	a m s **4.** _____
a m s **5.** _____	a m s **6.** _____

Build Fluency

Directions: Complete each sentence with a word from the box.

see	a

1. I can _____ *see* _____ Sam.

2. I see _____ *a* _____ man.

Directions: Write a sentence using each word.

3. | am |

I am I am.

4. | can |

I can see.

Write About It

Directions: Read "Sam" again. Draw a picture about the story. Write about your picture.

The Boy Wont go in The water

Fluency Check

Directions: Listen to the child read the list below. Mark one check in the green box if the word or letter-sound is read correctly (accuracy). Mark another check in the blue box if it is read automatically (fluency).

CUMULATIVE ASSESSMENT			
Lesson	Letter-sound/Word		
3	s	☐	☐
	m	☐	☐
	am	☐	☐
	Sam	☐	☐
2	a	☐	☐
	I	☐	☐
	m	☐	☐
	am	☐	☐
1	m	☐	☐
	a	☐	☐
	b	☐	☐
	s	☐	☐
Number Correct (accuracy): _____ /12			
Number Automatic (fluency): _____ /12			

Match Uppercase and Lowercase Letters

Directions: Say the letter names in each box.
Draw lines to match the uppercase letters and lowercase letters.

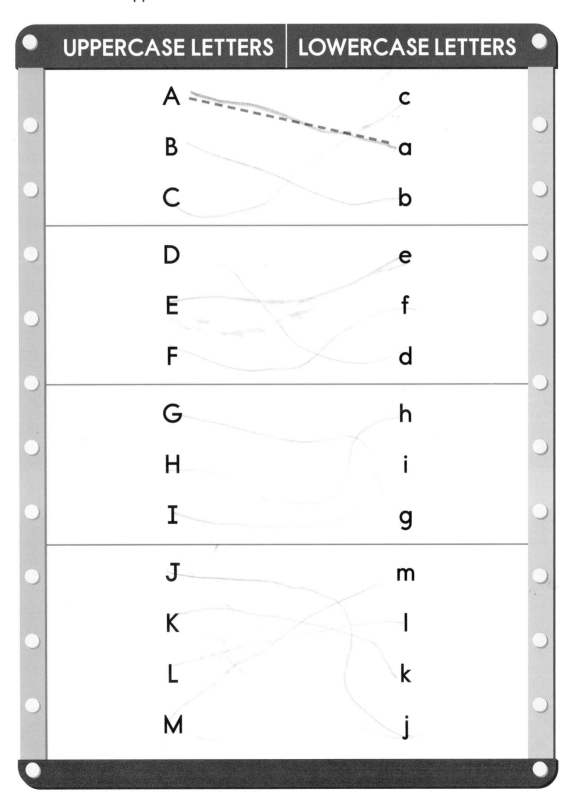

UPPERCASE LETTERS	LOWERCASE LETTERS
A	c
B	a
C	b
D	e
E	f
F	d
G	h
H	i
I	g
J	m
K	l
L	k
M	j

Directions: Say the letter names in each box.
Draw lines to match the uppercase letters and lowercase letters.

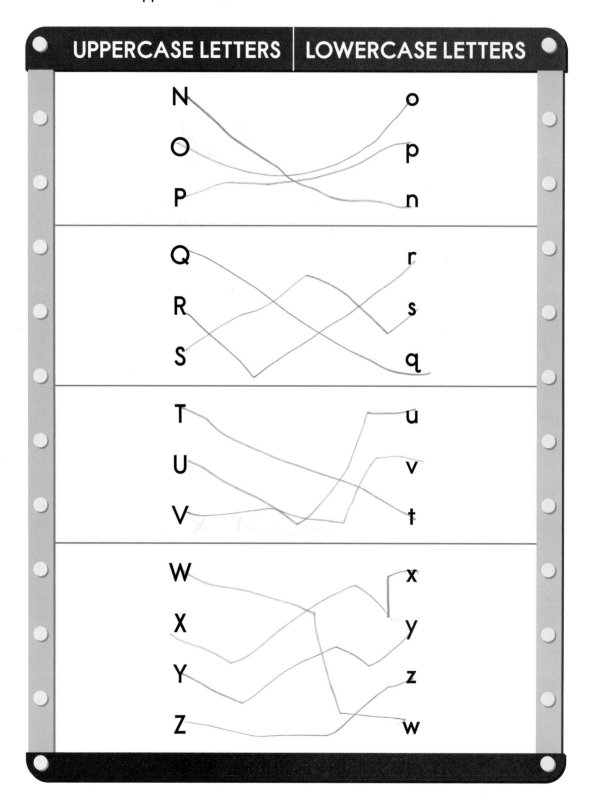

UPPERCASE LETTERS	LOWERCASE LETTERS
N	o
O	p
P	n
Q	r
R	s
S	q
T	u
U	v
V	t
W	x
X	y
Y	z
Z	w

Learn and Blend

Directions: **Listen and join in.**

t...t...t...
Tick-tock, goes the clock.

Tt

Blend It

Directions: **Chorally say the sounds and read the words.**

INTRODUCE

1. m	s	a	t
2. am	at	mat	sat

IN CONTEXT

3. I sat.

4. I sat on the mat.

Daily Practice

Directions: **Do one activity each day. Then check the box.**

☐ **Build Fluency** Read the words each day by yourself and to a partner.

☐ **Mark It** Circle all the words with t.

☐ **Sing It** Sing the "Alphabet Song" with a partner.

☐ **See It** Find words in your classroom with t.

Read-Spell-Write

Directions: Write each word two times. Say each letter as you write it.

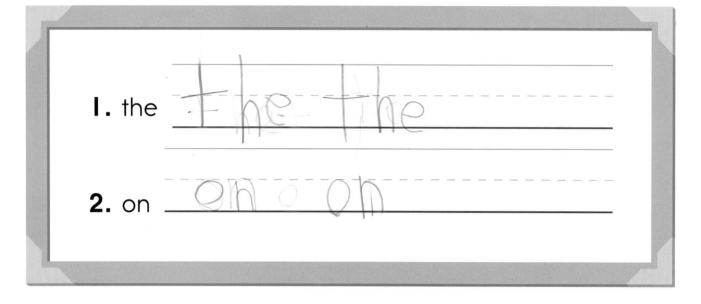

1. the   The the

2. on   on on

Use in Context

Directions: Complete each sentence with a word from above.
Read the finished sentences to a partner.

1. I can see ___the___ mat.

2. Sam sat ___on___ a mat.

Sam Sat

Name _____

Sam sat on the rock.

1

Sam sat on the mat.

4

2

Sam sat on the slide.

Sam sat on the cat!

3

Trace and Write

Directions: Trace and write the letters T and t. These letters stand for /t/. Say the sound each time you write the letter.

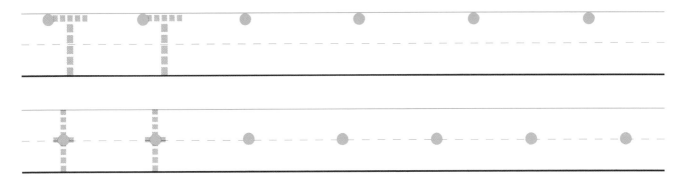

Directions: Say the name of the picture. Write Tt on the line if the picture name begins with /t/.

1. _____	2. _____	3. _____

4. _____	5. _____	6. _____

Think and Write

Directions: Write the first letter of the picture name.

1.  _____

2.  _____

3.  _____

4.  _____

Listen and Spell

Directions: Write each word and sentence that you hear.

1. _____

2. _____

Trace, Write, and Build

Directions: Trace and write each word.
Then build each word with letter cards.

TRACE	WRITE
on	
the	
at	
mat	
sat	

Sort It Out

Directions: Look at the pictures on page 387. Say each picture name. Then sort the pictures by beginning sound.

Ss

Tt

What words do you know with these sounds?

_____

_____

_____

_____

Read and Write

Directions: Say the picture name. Circle the first letter of the picture name.
Write the letter on the line.

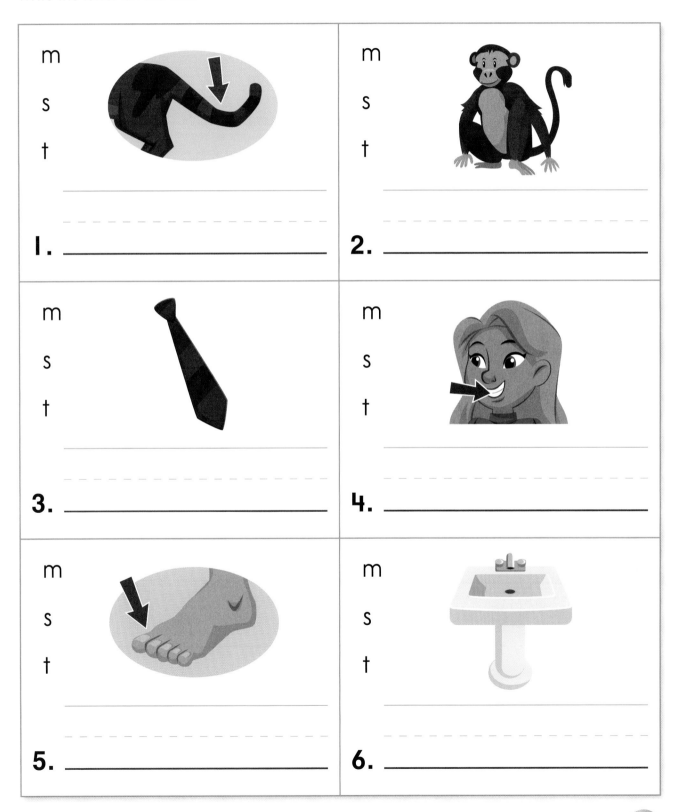

1.

2.

3.

4.

5.

6.

Build Fluency

Directions: Complete each sentence with a word from the box.

the	see

1. I _____ Sam.

2. I sat on _____ mat.

Directions: Write a sentence using each word.

3. sat _____

_____

_____

4. am _____

_____

_____

Write About It

Directions: Read "Sam Sat" again. Draw a picture that shows one place Sam sat. Write about your picture.

Fluency Check

Directions: Listen to the child read the list below. Mark one check in the green box if the word or letter-sound is read correctly (accuracy). Mark another check in the blue box if it is read automatically (fluency).

CUMULATIVE ASSESSMENT					
Lesson	Word/Letter-sound		Lesson	Word/Letter-Sound	
4	t ☐ ☐		**2**	a ☐ ☐	
	at ☐ ☐			I ☐ ☐	
	sat ☐ ☐			m ☐ ☐	
	mat ☐ ☐			am ☐ ☐	
3	s ☐ ☐		**1**	m ☐ ☐	
	m ☐ ☐			a ☐ ☐	
	am ☐ ☐			b ☐ ☐	
	Sam ☐ ☐			s ☐ ☐	

Number Correct (accuracy): _____ /16

Number Automatic (fluency): _____ /16

Match Uppercase and Lowercase Letters

Directions: Write the lowercase letter that goes with the uppercase letter.

1. b
d B _____
p

2. a
c O _____
o

3. b
d D _____
p

4. u
v V _____
y

5. c
e E _____
f

6. c
e C _____
p

7. k
d R _____
r

8. i
j J _____
q

9. d
p P _____
q

10. h
i L _____
l

11. s
v Z _____
z

12. v
x X _____
y

13. c
s S _____
z

14. o
p Q _____
q

15. f
t T _____
p

Directions: Write the lowercase letter that goes with the uppercase letter.

16. v

x Y ___

y

17. a

o A ___

v

18. m

n N ___

r

19. f

h H ___

k

20. u

v W ___

w

21. i

j I ___

t

22. f

k F ___

t

23. a

u U ___

v

24. g

p G ___

q

25. m

n M ___

w

26. f

h K ___

k

Directions: Write your name on the line below.

Learn and Blend

Directions: Listen and join in.

p…p…p…
Pop that popcorn
in the pot.

Pp

Blend It

Directions: Chorally say the sounds and read the words.

INTRODUCE

1. t   p   a   s

2. am   Pam   map   tap

IN CONTEXT

3. Pam sat.

4. I see a map.

Daily Practice

Directions: Do one activity each day. Then check the box.

☐ **Build Fluency** Read the words each day by yourself and to a partner.

☐ **Mark It** Circle all the words with **p**.

☐ **Sing It** Sing the "Alphabet Song" with a partner.

☐ **Write About It** Find words in your classroom with **p**.

Read-Spell-Write

Directions: Write each word two times. Say each letter as you write it.

1. like _____

2. to _____

Use in Context

Directions: Complete each sentence with a word from above.

1. I like _____ nap on a mat.

2. I _____ Sam.

Name _____

I Like

I am Sam.

Fold

I like to dance.
Tap. Tap. Tap.

4

2

I like to build.
Tap. Tap. Tap.

I am Pam.

3

Trace and Write

Directions: Trace and write the letters **P** and **p**. These letters stand for /p/. Say the sound each time you write the letter.

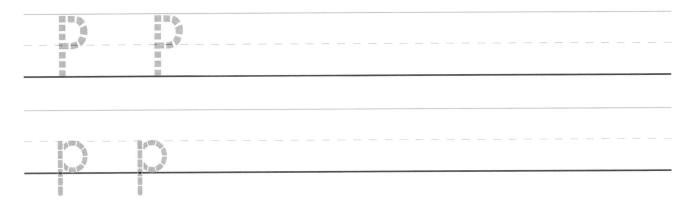

Directions: Say the name of the picture. Write **Pp** on the line if the picture name begins with /p/.

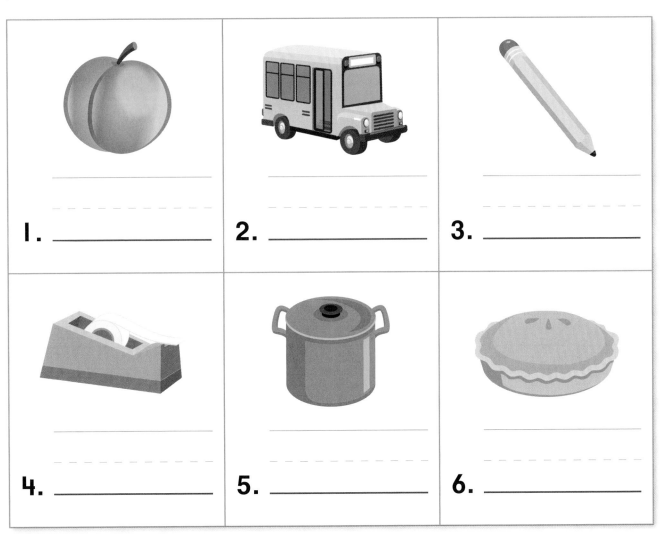

1. _____

2. _____

3. _____

4. _____

5. _____

6. _____

Think and Write

Directions: Listen to each picture name. Write the first letter of the picture name on the line.

1.

_____

2.

_____

3.

_____

4.

_____

Listen and Spell

Directions: Write each word and sentence that you hear.

1. _____

2. _____

Trace, Write, and Build

Directions: Trace and write each word.
Then build each word with letter cards.

TRACE	WRITE
like	
to	
pat	
map	
sat	

Sort It Out

Directions: Look at the pictures on page 387. Say each picture name. Then sort the pictures by beginning sound.

Pp	Tt

What words do you know with these sounds?

Read and Write

Directions: Say the picture name. Circle the first letter of the picture name.
Write the letter on the line.

p
s
t

1. _____

p
s
t

2. _____

p
s
t

3. _____

p
s
t

4. _____

p
s
t

5. _____

p
s
t

6. _____

Build Fluency

Directions: Complete each sentence with a word from the box.

the   to

1. I like _____ tap.

2. I sat on _____ mat.

Directions: Write a sentence using each word.

3. | pat | _____

_____

4. | map | _____

_____

Write About It

Directions: Read "I Like" again. Draw a picture that shows what Sam or Pam likes. Write about your picture.

Fluency Check

Directions: Listen to the child read the list below. Mark one check in the green box if the word or letter-sound is read correctly (accuracy). Mark another check in the blue box if it is read automatically (fluency).

CUMULATIVE ASSESSMENT									
Lesson	**Word/Letter-sound**				**Lesson**	**Word/Letter-sound**			
5	p	☐	☐		**2**	a	☐	☐	
	tap	☐	☐			I	☐	☐	
	map	☐	☐			m	☐	☐	
	Pam	☐	☐			am	☐	☐	
4	t	☐	☐		**1**	m	☐	☐	
	at	☐	☐			a	☐	☐	
	sat	☐	☐			b	☐	☐	
	mat	☐	☐			s	☐	☐	
3	s	☐	☐						
	m	☐	☐						
	am	☐	☐						
	Sam	☐	☐						

Number Correct (accuracy): _____ /20

Number Automatic (fluency): _____ /20

Dear Family,

In this unit, your child will learn about words that contain the short vowel **i**. He or she will learn to read words with the short vowel **i, n, c, f,** and **d** sounds, such as **sit; man; cat; fan;** and **dip.**

Home Connection

Read Connected Text

For each week's lesson, your child will read a Take-Home Book that focuses on the lesson skill. At week's end, the book will be sent home with your child. Read the book to your child, or read it aloud together, pointing to each word as you say it. Multiple readings will give your child practice with the lesson skill.

Practice with the Take-Home Book

Ask your child to point to words in the story that include the vowel or consonant sound for that lesson.

Have your child tell you about the book in one sentence. Write what your child says and read the description aloud together.

Lesson Skills and Take-Home Books

Lesson 6 **Nn:** "What Is It?"
Lesson 7 **Short i:** "Big and Little"
Lesson 8 **Cc:** "Good Cat"
Lesson 9 **Ff:** "Can It Fit?"
Lesson 10 **Dd:** "Dan and Dad"

Extend the Learning

With your child, look for words with short vowel **i** in books, signs, magazine covers, etc. Keep a notebook of words you discover.

Challenge your child to identify objects in your home or other locations that have a short vowel **i** sound. For example, "I spy a mitt."

 Visit SadlierConnect.com for Student & Family Resources.

Apreciada familia:

Conexión con el Hogar

En esta unidad, su niño(a) aprenderá palabras que contienen la vocal **i**. Aprenderá a leer palabras con el sonido corto de la **i**, y los sonidos de la **n**, de la **c**, de la **f** y de la **d**, tales como **sit; man; cat; fan** y **dip**.

Leyendo la historieta en el Take-Home Book

Para cada lección de la semana su niño(a) leerá un cuadernillo de historietas, Take-Home Book, que se enfoca en las destrezas de la lección. Al final de cada semana su niño(a) llevará el cuadernillo a la casa. Lea la historieta a su niño(a) o leánla en voz alta juntos, señalando cada palabra al decirla. Leer varias veces ayudará a su niño(a) a practicar las destrezas de la lección.

Practicando con el Take-Home Book

Pida a su niño(a) señalar en la historieta palabras que incluyan el sonido de la vocal o de la consonante para esa lección. Luego pídale que resuma la historieta en una frase. Escriba lo que dice su niño(a) y después lean juntos lo que escribió.

Lesson Skills and Take-Home Books

Lesson 6 **Nn:** "What Is It?"
Lesson 7 **Short i:** "Big and Little"
Lesson 8 **Cc:** "Good Cat"
Lesson 9 **Ff:** "Can It Fit?"
Lesson 10 **Dd:** "Dan and Dad"

Ampliando el aprendizaje

Con su niño(a) busque palabras con vocales con sonido corto de la **i** en libros, letreros, portadas de revistas, etc. Haga una libreta con palabras que descubran juntos.

Rete a su niño(a) a identificar, ya sea en su casa o en otros lugares, objetos que tengan el sonido corto de la vocal **i**. Por ejemplo: "I spy a mitt."

 Visite SadlierConnect.com **para recursos para el estudiante y la familia.**

Learn and Blend

Directions: Listen and join in.

n…n…n…
No. No. No!

Nn

Blend It

Directions: Chorally say the sounds and read the words.

INTRODUCE

1. n   p   t   a

2. an   man   pan   tan

REVIEW

3. map   sat   am   tap

CHALLENGE

4. pans   maps   naps   mats

IN CONTEXT

5. The man sat.

6. I see a pan.

Daily Practice

Directions: Do one activity each day. Then check the box.

☐ **Build Fluency** Read the words each day by yourself and to a partner.

☐ **Mark It** Circle all the words with n.

☐ **Spell It** Have a partner say each word. Write the word. Check your answer.

☐ **Write About It** Use the words to create a story. Draw a box around words from the list that you used.

Read-Spell-Write

Directions: Write each word two times. Say each letter as you write it.

1. is

2. it

Use in Context

Directions: Complete each sentence with a word from above.
Read the finished sentences to a partner.

1. The mat _____ tan.

2. Pat sat on _____.

1

Name _____

What Is It?

What is it?
It is a man.

Fold

What is it?
It is an apple pie.

4

2

What is it?
It is a pan.

What is it?
It is an apple.

3

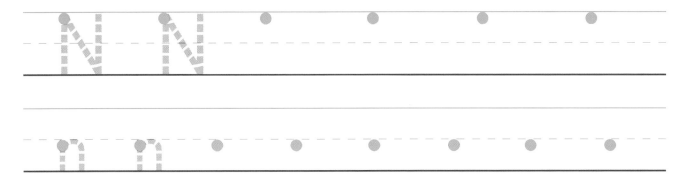

Trace and Write

Directions: Trace and write the letters **N** and **n**. These letters stand for /n/. Say the sound each time you write the letter.

Directions: Say the name of the picture. Write **Nn** on the line if the picture name begins with /n/.

1. _____

2. _____

3. _____

4. _____

5. _____

6. _____

Think and Write

Directions: Listen to each picture name. Write the first letter of the picture name on the line.

1.  _____

2.  _____

Directions: Listen to each picture name. Write the letter for each sound in a separate box.

3.

4.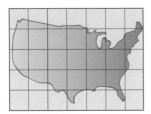

Listen and Spell

Directions: Write each word and sentence that you hear.

1. _____

2. _____

Trace, Write, and Build

Directions: Trace and write each word.
Then build each word with letter cards.

TRACE	WRITE
is	
it	
an	
man	
nap	

Sort It Out

Directions: Look at the pictures on page 389. Say each picture name. Then sort the pictures by beginning sound.

Mm

Nn

What words do you know with these sounds?

Read and Write

Directions: Say the picture name. Circle the first letter of the picture name.
Write the letter on the line.

m n p **1.** _____	m n p **2.** _____
m n p **3.** _____	m n p **4.** _____
m n p **5.** _____	m n p **6.** _____

Build Fluency

Directions: Complete each sentence with a word from the box.

is	to

1. I like _____ nap.

2. The mat _____ tan.

Directions: Write a sentence using each word.

3. pat _____
_____
_____

4. man _____
_____
_____

Write About It

Directions: Read "What Is It?" again. Draw a picture that shows one answer to "What Is it?" Write about your picture.

Fluency Check

Directions: Listen to the child read the list below. Mark one check in the green box if the word or letter-sound is read correctly (accuracy). Mark another check in the blue box if it is read automatically (fluency).

CUMULATIVE ASSESSMENT					
Lesson	Word/Letter-sound		Lesson	Word/Letter-sound	
6	man ☐ ☐		**3**	s ☐ ☐	
	pans ☐ ☐			m ☐ ☐	
	tan ☐ ☐			am ☐ ☐	
	nap ☐ ☐			Sam ☐ ☐	
5	p ☐ ☐		**2**	a ☐ ☐	
	tap ☐ ☐			I ☐ ☐	
	map ☐ ☐			m ☐ ☐	
	Pam ☐ ☐			am ☐ ☐	
4	t ☐ ☐		**1**	m ☐ ☐	
	at ☐ ☐			a ☐ ☐	
	sat ☐ ☐			b ☐ ☐	
	mat ☐ ☐			s ☐ ☐	

Number Correct (accuracy): _____ /24

Number Automatic (fluency): _____ /24

Learn and Blend

Directions: Listen and join in.

i…i…i…
Scratch an itchy itch.

Ii

Blend It

Directions: Chorally say the sounds and read the words.

INTRODUCE

1. i	a	n	p
2. it	sit	in	pin
3. is	tip	pit	pat

REVIEW

4. man	tap	sat	am

CHALLENGE

5. sits	taps	pats	naps

IN CONTEXT

6. I can sit.

7. It is a map.

Daily Practice

Directions: Do one activity each day. Then check the box.

☐ **Build Fluency** Read the words each day by yourself and to a partner.

☐ **Mark It** Circle all the words with it.

☐ **Spell It** Have a partner say each word. Write the word. Check your answer.

☐ **Write About It** Use the words to create a story. Draw a box around words from the list that you used.

Read-Spell-Write

Directions: Write each word two times. Say each letter as you write it.

1. big _____
2. little _____

Use in Context

Directions: Complete each sentence with a word from above.
Read the finished sentences to a partner.

1. The man is _____.
2. The pin is _____.

1

Name —————

Big and Little

It is big.
It is a tree.

— Fold —

It is little.
It is a pin.

4

2

It is little.
It is a flower.

It is big.
It is a dog.

3

Trace and Write

Directions: Trace and write the letters **I** and **i**. These letters stand for the short i sound. Say the sound each time you write the letter.

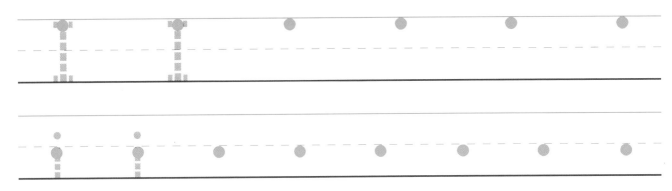

Directions: Say the name of the picture. Write **Ii** on the line if the picture name has the short i sound.

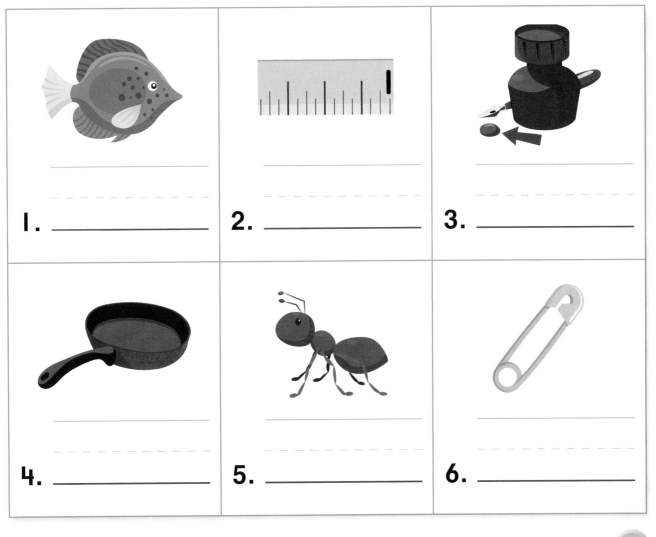

1. _____

2. _____

3. _____

4. _____

5. _____

6. _____

Think and Write

Directions: Listen to each picture name. Write the first letter of the picture name on the line.

1.  _____

2.  _____

Directions: Listen to each picture name. Write the letter for each sound in a separate box.

3.

4.

Listen and Spell

Directions: Write each word and sentence that you hear.

1. _____

_____

2. _____

Trace, Write, and Build

Directions: Trace and write each word.
Then build each word with letter cards.

TRACE	WRITE
big	
little	
in	
sit	
pin	

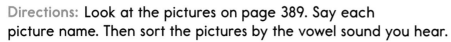

Sort It Out

Directions: Look at the pictures on page 389. Say each picture name. Then sort the pictures by the vowel sound you hear.

Short a	Short i

What words do you know with these sounds?

_____

_____

_____

Read and Write

Directions: Say the picture name. Circle the letter **a** if the name has the
short a sound. Circle the letter **i** if the name has the **short i** sound.
Write the letter on the line.

a

i

1. _____

a

i

2. _____

a

i

3. _____

a

i

4. _____

a

i

5. _____

a

i

6. _____

Build Fluency

Directions: Complete each sentence with a word from the box.

it big

1. I can see _____.

2. The map is _____.

Directions: Write a sentence using each word.

3. | sit | _____

4. | nap | _____

Write About It

Directions: Read "Big and Little" again. Draw a picture that shows one big or little thing. Write about your picture.

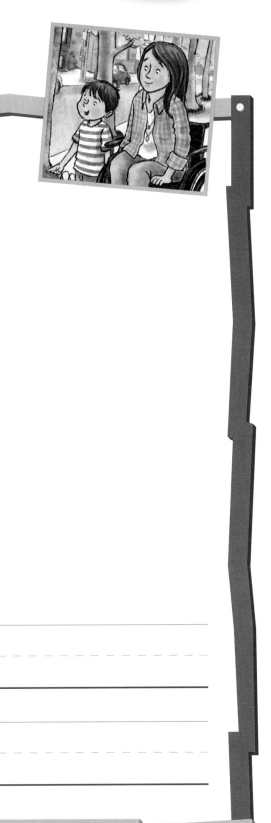

Fluency Check

Directions: Listen to the child read the list below. Mark one check in the green box if the word or letter-sound is read correctly (accuracy). Mark another check in the blue box if it is read automatically (fluency).

Lesson	Word/Letter-sound			Lesson	Word/Letter-sound		
7	it	☐	☐	4	t	☐	☐
	tip	☐	☐		at	☐	☐
	sits	☐	☐		sat	☐	☐
	pin	☐	☐		mat	☐	☐
6	man	☐	☐	3	s	☐	☐
	pans	☐	☐		m	☐	☐
	tan	☐	☐		am	☐	☐
	nap	☐	☐		Sam	☐	☐
5	p	☐	☐	2	a	☐	☐
	tap	☐	☐		I	☐	☐
	map	☐	☐		m	☐	☐
	Pam	☐	☐		am	☐	☐

Number Correct (accuracy): _____ /24

Number Automatic (fluency): _____ /24

Learn and Blend

Directions: Listen and join in.

c...c...c...
The cook cuts the cake.

Cc

Blend It

Directions: Chorally say the sounds and read the words.

INTRODUCE

1. c   a   i   n

2. cat   sat   cap   tap

3. sick   pick   sack   pack

REVIEW

4. sit   sat   man   map

CHALLENGE

5. pick   picking   pack   packing

IN CONTEXT

6. I can sit.

7. I like the cat.

Daily Practice

Directions: Do one activity each day. Then check the box.

☐ **Build Fluency** Read the words each day by yourself and to a partner.

☐ **Mark It** Circle all the words with c.

☐ **Spell It** Have a partner say each word. Write the word. Check your answer.

☐ **Write About It** Use the words to create a story. Draw a box around words from the list that you used.

Read-Spell-Write

Directions: Write each word two times. Say each letter as you write it.

1. my _____

2. good _____

Use in Context

Directions: Complete each sentence with a word from above.
Read the finished sentences to a partner.

1. I like _____ cat.

2. The cat is _____.

1

Name _____

Good Cat

— Fold —

My cat is little.
My cat is black.

— Fold —

My cat is gray.
My cat is good.

4

2

My cat is big.
My cat is white.

My cat is brown.
My cat is hungry!

3

Trace and Write

Directions: Trace and write the letters C and c. These letters stand for /k/. Say the sound each time you write the letter.

C C

c c

Directions: Say the name of the picture. Write Cc on the line if the picture name begins with /k/.

1. _____

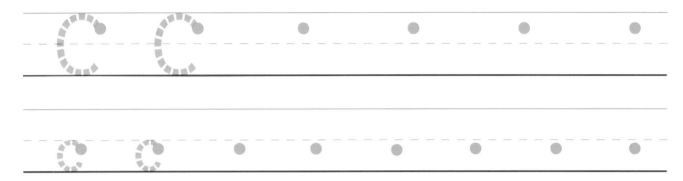

2. _____

9

3. _____

4. _____

5. _____

6. _____

Think and Write

Directions: Listen to each picture name. Write the first letter of the picture name on the line.

1.  _____

2.  _____

Directions: Listen to each picture name. Write the letter for each sound in a separate box.

3.

4.

Listen and Spell

Directions: Write each word and sentence that you hear.

1. _____

2. _____

Trace, Write, and Build

Directions: Trace and write each word.
Then build each word with letter cards.

TRACE	WRITE
my	
good	
sick	
cat	
pick	

Sort It Out

Directions: Look at the pictures on page 389. Say each picture name. Then sort the pictures by begininng sound.

Cc	Pp

What words do you know with these sounds?

Read and Write

Independent Practice

Directions: Say the picture name. Circle the first letter of the picture name. Write the letter on the line.

c
p
s

1. _____

c
p
s

2. _____

c
p
s

3. _____

c
p
s

4. _____

c
p
s

5. _____

c
p
s

6. _____

Build Fluency

Directions: Complete each sentence with a word from the box.

is	good

1. My cat _____ big.

2. It is a _____ cat.

Directions: Write a sentence using each word.

3. sick _____

_____

4. cap _____

_____

Write About It

Directions: Read "Good Cat" again.
Draw a picture about one of the cats. Write about your picture.

Fluency Check

Directions: Listen to the child read the list below. Mark one check in the green box if the word or letter-sound is read correctly (accuracy). Mark another check in the blue box if it is read automatically (fluency).

CUMULATIVE ASSESSMENT							
Lesson	Word			Lesson	Word/Letter-sound		
8	cat	☐	☐	**5**	p	☐	☐
	can	☐	☐		tap	☐	☐
	sick	☐	☐		map	☐	☐
	pack	☐	☐		Pam	☐	☐
7	it	☐	☐	**4**	t	☐	☐
	tip	☐	☐		at	☐	☐
	sits	☐	☐		sat	☐	☐
	pin	☐	☐		mat	☐	☐
6	man	☐	☐	**3**	s	☐	☐
	pans	☐	☐		m	☐	☐
	tan	☐	☐		am	☐	☐
	nap	☐	☐		Sam	☐	☐

Number Correct (accuracy): _____ /24

Number Automatic (fluency): _____ /24

Learn and Blend

Directions: Listen and join in.

f...f...f...
Feel the fan on
your face.

Ff

Blend It

Directions: Chorally say the sounds and read the words.

INTRODUCE

1. f   c   a   i

2. fan   fat   fit   if

REVIEW

3. can   sick   pin   man

4. Pam   mat   am   sat

CHALLENGE

5. fans   cats   caps   pans

IN CONTEXT

6. The cat is fat.

7. Can it fit?

Daily Practice

Directions: Do one activity each day. Then check the box.

☐ **Build Fluency** Read the words each day by yourself and to a partner.

☐ **Mark It** Circle all the words with f.

☐ **Spell It** Have a partner say each word. Write the word. Check your answer.

☐ **Write About It** Use the words to create a story. Draw a box around words from the list that you used.

Read-Spell-Write

Directions: Write each word two times. Say each letter as you write it.

1. yes

2. no

Use in Context

Directions: Complete each sentence with a word from above.
Read the finished sentences to a partner.

1. Is a pin big? _____!

2. Is a pin little? _____!

Name _____

Can It Fit?

The cat is little.
Can it fit? Yes!

1

The elephant is big.
Can it fit? No!

4

2

The fish is fat.
Can it fit? No!

Fold

Fold

The cow is little.
Can it fit? Yes!

3

Trace and Write

Directions: Trace and write the letters F and f. These letters stand for /f/. Say the sound each time you write the letter.

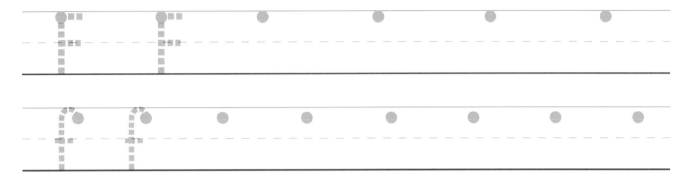

Directions: Say the name of the picture. Write Ff on the line if the picture name begins with /f/.

1. _____	2. _____	3. _____

4. _____	5. _____	6. _____

Dictation

Think and Write

Directions: Listen to each picture name. Write the first letter of the picture name on the line.

1.

_____

2.

_____

Directions: Listen to each picture name. Write the letter for each sound in a separate box.

3.

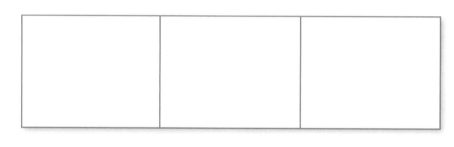

4.

Listen and Spell

Directions: Write each word and sentence that you hear.

1. _____

2. _____

Trace, Write, and Build

Directions: Trace and write each word.
Then build each word with letter cards.

TRACE	WRITE
yes	
no	
if	
fat	
fit	

Sort It Out

Directions: Look at the pictures on page 389. Say each picture name. Then sort the pictures by beginning sound.

Ff

Tt

What words do you know with these sounds?

_____

_____

Read and Write

Directions: Say the picture name. Circle the first letter of the picture name. Write the letter on the line.

f
s
t

1. _____

f
s
t

2. _____

f
s
t

3. _____

f
s
t

4. _____

f
s
t

5. _____

f
s
t

6. _____

Build Fluency

Directions: Complete each sentence with a word from the box.

yes	good

1. _____, I like it.

2. My cat is _____.

Directions: Write a sentence using each word.

3. fit _____

4. can _____

Write About It

Directions: Read "Can It Fit?" again. Draw a picture that shows one thing that can fit. Write about your picture.

Fluency Check

Directions: Listen to the child read the list below. Mark one check in the green box if the word or letter-sound is read correctly (accuracy). Mark another check in the blue box if it is read automatically (fluency).

CUMULATIVE ASSESSMENT							
Lesson	Word			Lesson	Word/Letter-sound		
9	fat	☐	☐	6	man	☐	☐
	fan	☐	☐		pans	☐	☐
	if	☐	☐		tan	☐	☐
	fit	☐	☐		nap	☐	☐
8	cat	☐	☐	5	p	☐	☐
	can	☐	☐		tap	☐	☐
	sick	☐	☐		map	☐	☐
	pack	☐	☐		Pam	☐	☐
7	it	☐	☐	4	t	☐	☐
	tip	☐	☐		at	☐	☐
	sits	☐	☐		sat	☐	☐
	pin	☐	☐		mat	☐	☐

Number Correct (accuracy): _____ /24

Number Automatic (fluency): _____ /24

Learn and Blend

Directions: Listen and join in.

d...d...d...
Dig in the dirt.

Dd

Blend It

Directions: Chorally say the sounds and read the words.

INTRODUCE

1. d	f	a	i
2. dad	sad	did	dip

REVIEW

3. fat	cat	pick	tan
4. tap	at	am	sat

CHALLENGE

5. Dan's	Sam's	Pam's	Pat's

IN CONTEXT

6. Dan is sad.

7. I did it!

Daily Practice

Directions: Do one activity each day. Then check the box.

- ☐ **Build Fluency** Read the words each day by yourself and to a partner.
- ☐ **Mark It** Circle all the words with d.
- ☐ **Spell It** Have a partner say each word. Write the word. Check your answer.
- ☐ **Write About It** Use the words to create a story. Draw a box around words from the list that you used.

Read-Spell-Write

Directions: Write each word two times. Say each letter as you write it.

1. look _____

2. he _____

Use in Context

Directions: Complete each sentence with a word from above.
Read the finished sentences to a partner.

1. _____ at the map.

2. _____ is sad.

—

Name _____

Dan and Dad

Fold

Look at Dan.
He is wet.

Fold

Look at Dad.
He is happy.

4

2

Look at Dad.
He is sad.

Look at Dan.
He is dry.

3

Trace and Write

Directions: Trace and write the letters **D** and **d**. These letters stand for /d/. Say the sound each time you write the letter.

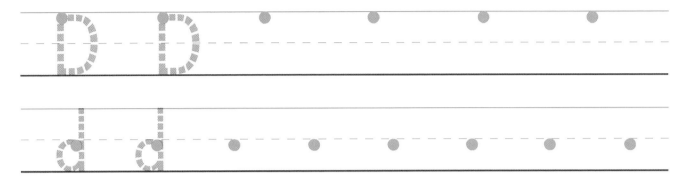

Directions: Say the name of the picture. Write **Dd** on the line if the picture name begins with /d/.

1. _____

2. _____

3. _____

4. _____

5. _____

6. _____

Think and Write

Directions: Listen to each picture name. Write the first letter of the picture name on the line.

1.  ____

2.  ____

Directions: Listen to each picture name. Write the letter for each sound in a separate box.

3.

4.

Listen and Spell

Directions: Write each word and sentence that you hear.

1. ____

2. ____

Trace, Write, and Build

Directions: Trace and write each word. Then build each word with letter cards.

TRACE	WRITE
look	
he	
dad	
did	
sad	

Sort It Out

Directions: Look at the pictures on page 389. Say each picture name. Then sort the pictures by beginning sound.

Dd	Tt

What words do you know with these sounds?

Read and Write

Directions: Say the picture name. Circle the first letter of the picture name.
Write the letter on the line.

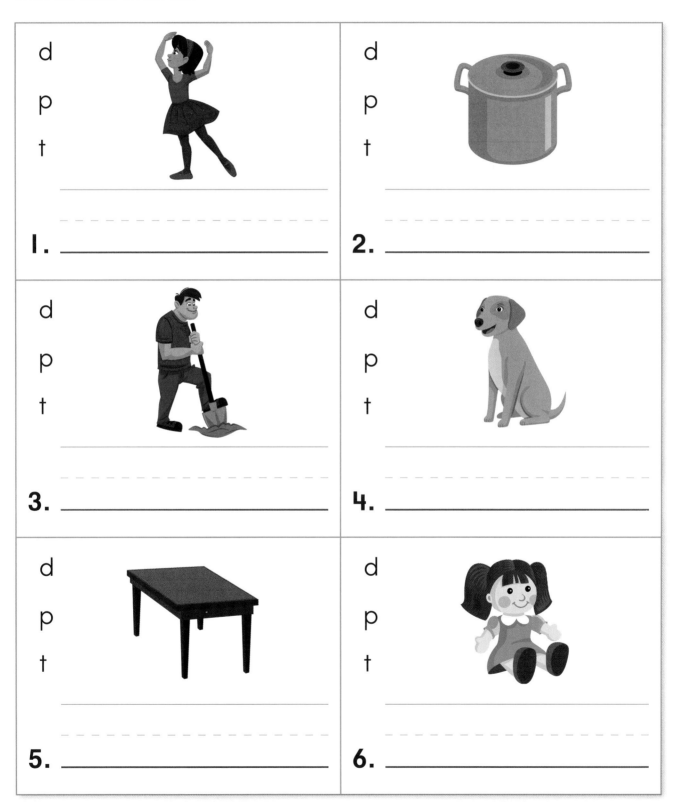

d
p
t

1. _____

d
p
t

2. _____

d
p
t

3. _____

d
p
t

4. _____

d
p
t

5. _____

d
p
t

6. _____

Build Fluency

Directions: Complete each sentence with a word from the box.

my	he

1. _____ is a man.

2. Dad likes _____ map.

Directions: Write a sentence using each word.

3. did _____

_____

4. fat _____

_____

Write About It

Directions: **Read "Dan and Dad" again.**
Draw a picture about Dan and Dad. Write about your picture.

Fluency Check

Directions: Listen to the child read the list below. Mark one check in the green box if the word or letter-sound is read correctly (accuracy). Mark another check in the blue box if it is read automatically (fluency).

CUMULATIVE ASSESSMENT							
Lesson	Word			Lesson	Word/Letter-sound		
10	dad	☐	☐	7	it	☐	☐
	did	☐	☐		tip	☐	☐
	sad	☐	☐		sits	☐	☐
	dip	☐	☐		pin	☐	☐
9	fat	☐	☐	6	man	☐	☐
	fan	☐	☐		pans	☐	☐
	if	☐	☐		tan	☐	☐
	fit	☐	☐		nap	☐	☐
8	cat	☐	☐	5	p	☐	☐
	can	☐	☐		tap	☐	☐
	sick	☐	☐		map	☐	☐
	pack	☐	☐		Pam	☐	☐
Number Correct (accuracy): _____ /24							
Number Automatic (fluency): _____ /24							

Dear Family,

In this unit, your child will learn about words that contain short vowel **o**. He or she will learn to read words with the short vowel **o, h, r, b,** and **l** sounds, such as **mop; had; rat; bat;** and **hill.**

Read Connected Text

For each week's lesson, your child will read a Take-Home Book that focuses on the lesson skill. At week's end, the book will be sent home with your child. Read the book to your child, or read it aloud together, pointing to each word as you say it. Multiple readings will give your child practice with the lesson skill.

Practice with the Take-Home Book

Ask your child to point to words in the story that include the vowel or consonant sound for that lesson.

Have your child tell you about the book in one sentence. Write what your child says and read the description aloud together.

Lesson Skills and Take-Home Books

Lesson 11 **Hh:** "Hats"
Lesson 12 **Short o:** "What Is This?"
Lesson 13 **Rr:** "Uh-oh!"
Lesson 14 **Bb:** "Good or Bad?"
Lesson 15 **Ll:** "Up and Down"

Extend the Learning

With your child, look for words with short vowel **o** in books, signs, magazine covers, etc. Keep a notebook of words you discover.

Challenge your child to identify objects in your home or other locations that have a short vowel **o** sound. For example, "I spy a mop."

 Visit SadlierConnect.com for Student & Family Resources.

Apreciada familia:

En esta unidad, su niño(a) aprenderá palabras que contienen la vocal **o**. Aprenderá a leer palabras con el sonido corto de la **o**, y los sonidos de la **h**, de la **r**, de la **b** y de la **l**, tales como **mop; ham; rat; bat** y **hill**.

Leyendo la historieta en el Take-Home Book

Para cada lección de la semana su niño(a) leerá un cuadernillo de historietas, Take-Home Book, que se enfoca en las destrezas de la lección. Al final de cada semana su niño(a) llevará el cuadernillo a la casa. Lea la historieta a su niño(a) o leánla en voz alta juntos, señalando cada palabra al decirla. Leer varias veces ayudará a su niño(a) a practicar las destrezas de la lección.

Practicando con el Take-Home Book

Pida a su niño(a) señalar en la historieta palabras que incluyan el sonido de la vocal o de la consonante para esa lección. Luego pídale que resuma la historieta en una frase. Escriba lo que dice su niño(a) y después lean juntos lo que escribió.

Lesson Skills and Take-Home Books

Lesson 11 **Hh:** "Hats"
Lesson 12 **Short o:** "What Is This?"
Lesson 13 **Rr:** "Uh-oh!"
Lesson 14 **Bb:** "Good or Bad?"
Lesson 15 **Ll:** "Up and Down"

Ampliando el aprendizaje

Con su niño(a) busque palabras con vocales con sonido corto de la **o** en libros, letreros, portadas de revistas, etc. Haga una libreta con palabras que descubran juntos.

Rete a su niño(a) a identificar, ya sea en su casa o en otros lugares, objetos que tengan el sonido corto de la vocal **o**. Por ejemplo: "I spy a mop."

 Visite **SadlierConnect.com** para recursos para el estudiante y la familia.

Learn and Blend

Directions: Listen and join in.

h...h...h...
Hands up.
It's so hot in here!

Hh

Blend It

Directions: Chorally say the sounds and read the words.

INTRODUCE

1. h   i   d   a

2. hat   sat   mat   cat

3. had   has   his   hit

REVIEW

4. did   mad   fan   can

CHALLENGE

5. hats   hits   fans   maps

IN CONTEXT

6. Dad has a hat.

7. I hid in it.

Daily Practice

Directions: Do one activity each day. Then check the box.

☐ **Build Fluency** Read the words each day by yourself and to a partner.

☐ **Mark It** Circle all the words with h.

☐ **Spell It** Have a partner say each word. Write the word. Check your answer.

☐ **Write About It** Use the words to create a story. Draw a box around words from the list that you used.

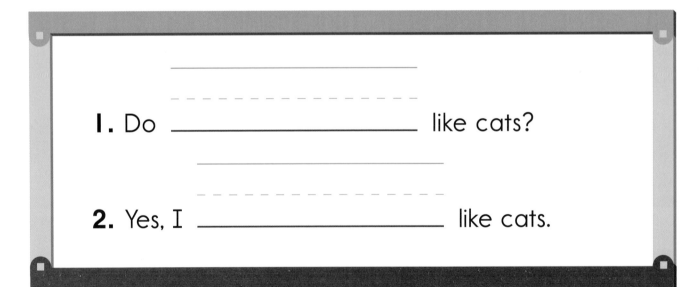

Read-Spell-Write

Directions: Write each word two times. Say each letter as you write it.

1. do _____

2. you _____

Use in Context

Directions: Complete each sentence with a word from above.
Read the finished sentences to a partner.

1. Do _____ like cats?

2. Yes, I _____ like cats.

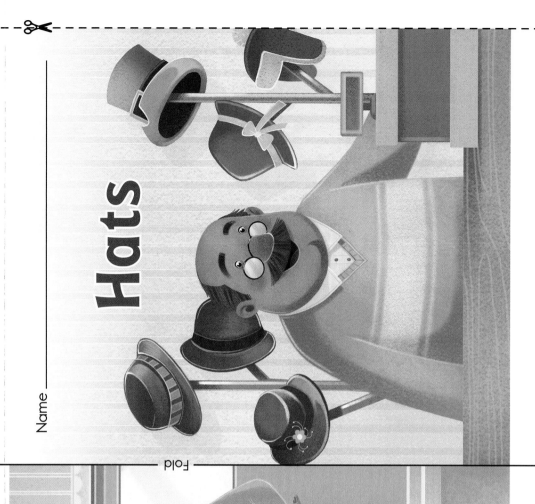

Name _____

Hats

1

Dan has hats.
Red hats. Blue hats.

Do you like his hat?
I do!

4

Big hats. Little hats.
Do you like his hats?

Sam looks at the hats.
He picks a big hat.

3

Trace and Write

Directions: Trace and write the letters H and h. These letters stand for /h/. Say the sound each time you write the letter.

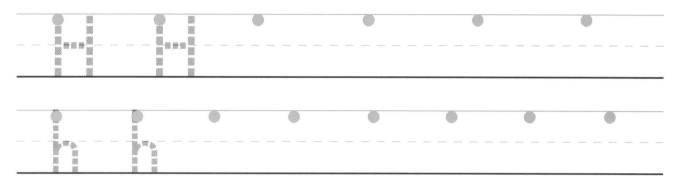

Directions: Say the name of the picture. Write **Hh** on the line if the picture name begins with /h/.

1. _____	2. _____	3. _____
		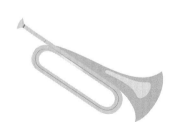
4. _____	5. _____	6. _____

Think and Write

Directions: Listen to each picture name. Write the first letter of the picture name on the line.

1.  _____

2.  _____

Directions: Listen to each picture name. Write the letter for each sound in a separate box.

3.

4.

Listen and Spell

Directions: Write each word and sentence that you hear.

1. _____

2. _____

Trace, Write, and Build

Directions: Trace and write each word.
Then build each word with letter cards.

TRACE	WRITE
do	
you	
hat	
had	
his	

Sort It Out

Directions: Look at the pictures on page 391. Say each picture name. Then sort the pictures by beginning sound.

Cc	Hh

What words do you know with these sounds?

Read and Write

Directions: Say the picture name. Circle the first letter of the picture name. Write the letter on the line.

1.
f
h
p

_____

2.
d
h
t

_____

3.
h
p
s

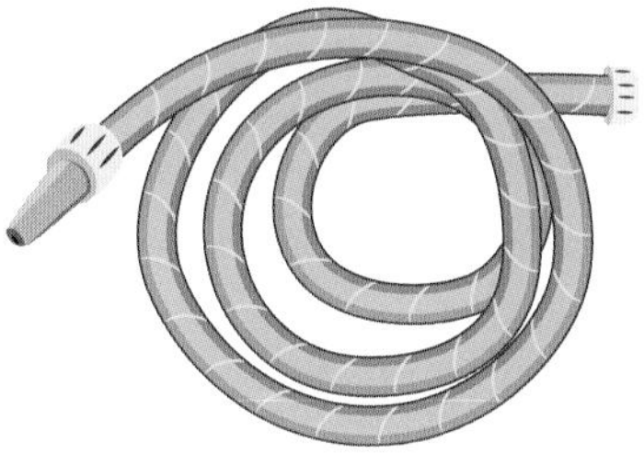

_____

4.
h
n
p

_____

5.
d
h
n

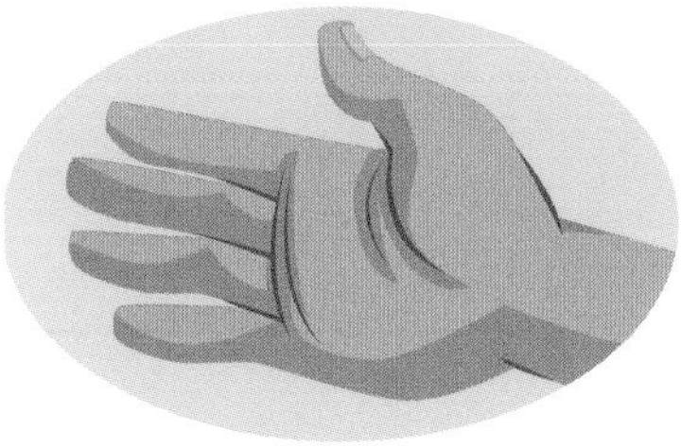

_____

6.
h
m
r

_____

Build Fluency

Directions: Complete each sentence with a word from the box.

do   look

1. _____ at the map.

2. I _____ see it.

Directions: Write a sentence using each word.

3. | has | _____

_____

4. | Dad | _____

_____

Write About It

Directions: Read "Hats" again. Draw a picture about Dan's hats. Write about your picture.

Fluency Check

Directions: Listen to the child read the list below. Mark one check in the green box if the word is read correctly (accuracy). Mark another check in the blue box if it is read automatically (fluency).

CUMULATIVE ASSESSMENT							
Lesson	**Word**			**Lesson**	**Word**		
11	has	☐	☐	**8**	cat	☐	☐
	hats	☐	☐		can	☐	☐
	him	☐	☐		sick	☐	☐
	hid	☐	☐		pack	☐	☐
10	dad	☐	☐	**7**	it	☐	☐
	did	☐	☐		tip	☐	☐
	sad	☐	☐		sits	☐	☐
	dip	☐	☐		pin	☐	☐
9	fat	☐	☐	**6**	man	☐	☐
	fan	☐	☐		pans	☐	☐
	if	☐	☐		tan	☐	☐
	fit	☐	☐		nap	☐	☐

Number Correct (accuracy): _____ /24

Number Automatic (fluency): _____ /24

Learn and Blend

Directions: Listen and join in.

o...o...o...
Turn the light on.

Blend It

Directions: Chorally say the sounds and read the words.

INTRODUCE

1. o	a	i	h
2. mop	top	hot	not
3. on	top	pop	dot

REVIEW

4. hat	sad	fan	can

CHALLENGE

5. mops	dots	pots	cats

IN CONTEXT

6. The cat sat on the mat.

7. It is hot!

Daily Practice

Directions: Do one activity each day. Then check the box.

☐ Build Fluency Read the words each day by yourself and to a partner.

☐ Mark It Circle all the words with ot.

☐ Spell It Have a partner say each word. Write the word. Check your answer.

☐ Write About It Use the words to create a story. Draw a box around words from the list that you used.

Read-Spell-Write

Directions: Write each word two times. Say each letter as you write it.

1. what _____

2. this _____

Use in Context

Directions: Complete each sentence with a word from above.
Read the finished sentences to a partner.

1. _____ is it?

2. Is _____ my hat?

1

Name _____

What Is This?

Pop! Pop! Pop!

Mom!

What is this?

Hop! Hop! Hop!

It is a frog.

I like it!

4

2

It is hot.
I like it!

Mom!
Look on the log.
What is this?

3

Trace and Write

Directions: Trace and write the letters O and o. These letters stand for /o/. Say the sound each time you write the letter.

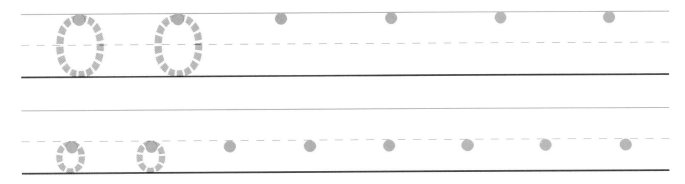

Directions: Say the name of the picture. Write Oo on the line if the picture name has the short o sound.

1. _____

2. _____

3. _____

4. _____

5. _____

6. _____

Think and Write

Directions: Listen to each picture name. Write the first letter of the picture name on the line.

1.  _____

2.  _____

Directions: Listen to each picture name. Write the letter for each sound in a separate box.

3.

4.

Listen and Spell

Directions: Write each word and sentence that you hear.

1. _____

2. _____

Trace, Write, and Build

Directions: Trace and write each word.
Then build each word with letter cards.

TRACE	WRITE
what	
this	
not	
hot	
on	

Sort It Out

Directions: Look at the pictures on page 391. Say each picture name. Then sort the pictures by the vowel sound.

Short a	Short o

What words do you know with these sounds?

Read and Write

Directions: Say the picture name. Circle the letter for the vowel sound you hear. Write the letter on the line.

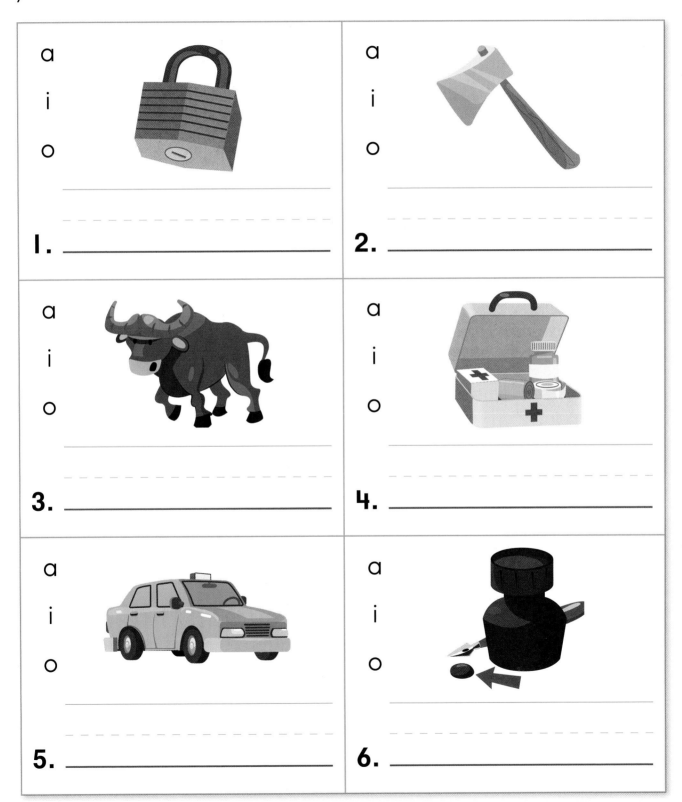

a
i
o

1. _____

a
i
o

2. _____

a
i
o

3. _____

a
i
o

4. _____

a
i
o

5. _____

a
i
o

6. _____

Build Fluency

Directions: Complete each sentence with a word from the box.

you	what

1. Did _____ see it?

2. _____ do you like?

Directions: Write a sentence using each word.

3. not _____

_____

_____

4. hot _____

_____

_____

Write About It

Directions: Read "What Is This?" again. Draw a picture that shows one answer to the question "What Is This?" Write about your picture.

Fluency Check

Directions: Listen to the child read the list below. Mark one check in the green box if the word is read correctly (accuracy). Mark another check in the blue box if it is read automatically (fluency).

CUMULATIVE ASSESSMENT

Lesson	Word			Lesson	Word		
12	on	☐	☐	9	fat	☐	☐
	mom	☐	☐		fan	☐	☐
	top	☐	☐		if	☐	☐
	not	☐	☐		fit	☐	☐
11	has	☐	☐	8	cat	☐	☐
	hats	☐	☐		can	☐	☐
	him	☐	☐		sick	☐	☐
	hid	☐	☐		pack	☐	☐
10	dad	☐	☐	7	it	☐	☐
	did	☐	☐		tip	☐	☐
	sad	☐	☐		sits	☐	☐
	dip	☐	☐		pin	☐	☐

Number Correct (accuracy): _____ /24

Number Automatic (fluency): _____ /24

Learn and Blend

Directions: Listen and join in.

r...r...r...
Ready...set...race
'round the racetrack!

Rr

Blend It

Directions: Chorally say the sounds and read the words.

INTRODUCE

1. r	o	i	h
2. ran	man	mat	rat
3. rip	tip	rock	sock

REVIEW

4. mom	hot	had	did

CHALLENGE

5. rocks	rips	pots	mops

IN CONTEXT

6. I ran.

7. Sit on the rock.

Daily Practice

Directions: Do one activity each day. Then check the box.

☐ Build Fluency Read the words each day by yourself and to a partner.

☐ Mark It Circle all the words with r.

☐ Spell It Have a partner say each word. Write the word. Check your answer.

☐ Write About It Use the words to create a story. Draw a box around words from the list that you used.

Read-Spell-Write

Directions: Write each word two times. Say each letter as you write it.

1. and _____

2. under _____

Use in Context

Directions: Complete each sentence with a word from above.
Read the finished sentences to a partner.

1. Ron _____ Sam ran.

2. The cat hid _____ my hat!

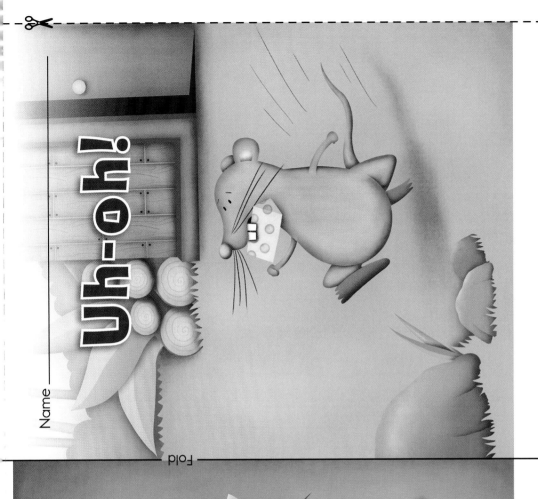

Uh-oh!

Name _____

1

The rat got the cheese.

He ran to the rock.

The rat ran under a cat.

Uh-oh!

4

2

The rat ran under a bush.

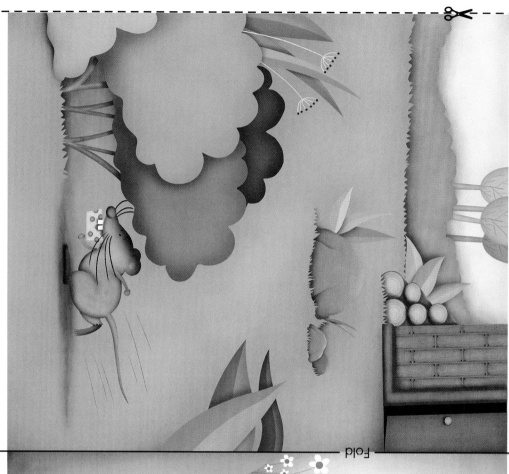

The rat ran and ran.
He ran under a chair.

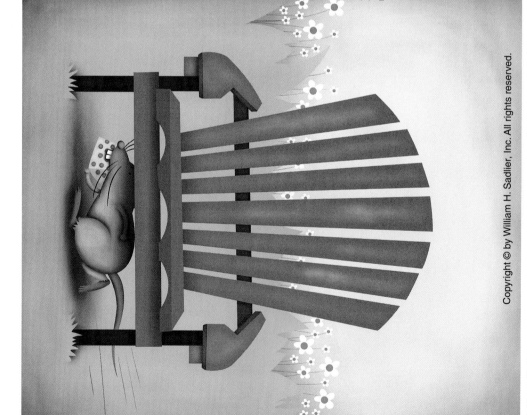

3

Trace and Write

Directions: Trace and write the letters R and r. These letters stand for /r/. Say the sound each time you write the letter.

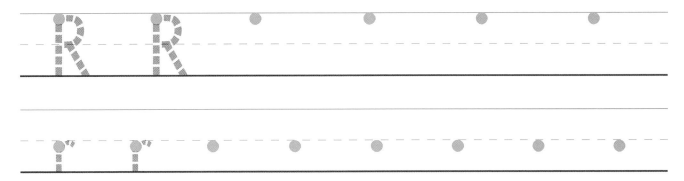

Directions: Say the name of the picture. Write Rr on the line if the picture name begins with /r/.

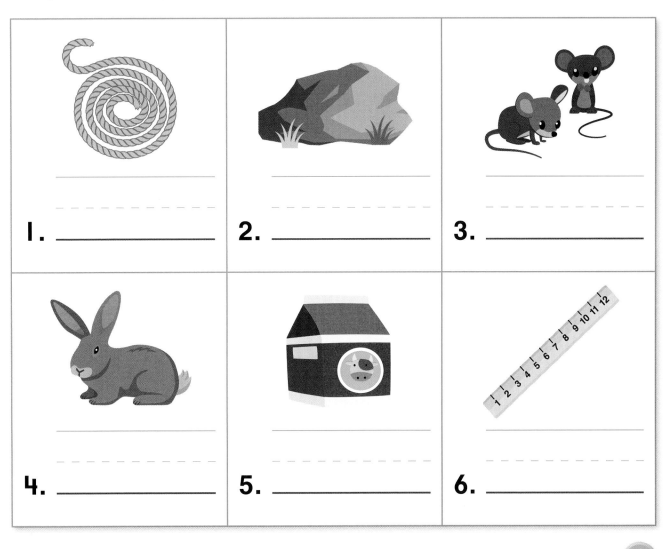

1. _____

2. _____

3. _____

4. _____

5. _____

6. _____

Think and Write

Directions: Listen to each picture name. Write the first letter of the picture name on the line.

1.  _____

2.  _____

Directions: Listen to each picture name. Write the letter for each sound in a separate box.

3.

4.

Listen and Spell

Directions: Write each word and sentence that you hear.

1. _____

2. _____

Trace, Write, and Build

Directions: Trace and write each word.
Then build each word with letter cards.

TRACE	WRITE
and	
under	
ran	
rip	
rock	

Sort It Out

Directions: Look at the pictures on page 391. Say each picture name. Then sort the pictures by beginning sound.

Ff	Rr

What words do you know with these sounds?

_____

_____

_____

_____

Read and Write

Directions: Say the picture name. Circle the first letter of the picture name.
Write the letter on the line.

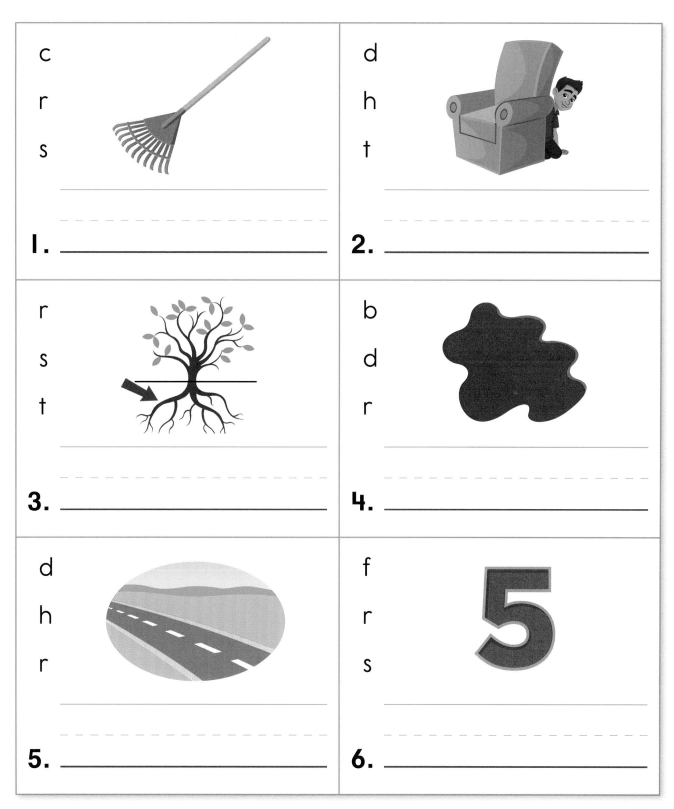

c
r
s

1. _____

d
h
t

2. _____

r
s
t

3. _____

b
d
r

4. _____

d
h
r

5. _____

f
r
s

6. _____

Independent
Practice

Build Fluency

Directions: Complete each sentence with a word from the box.

under	this

1. _____ is my cap.

2. My cap is _____ the sack.

Directions: Write a sentence using each word.

3. | rock | _____

   _____

4. | pot | _____

   _____

Write About It

Directions: Read "Uh-oh!" again. Draw a picture about the rat. Write about your picture.

Fluency Check

Directions: Listen to the child read the list below. Mark one check in the green box if the word is read correctly (accuracy). Mark another check in the blue box if it is read automatically (fluency).

Lesson	Word			Lesson	Word		
13	ran	☐	☐	**10**	dad	☐	☐
	rats	☐	☐		did	☐	☐
	rip	☐	☐		sad	☐	☐
	rock	☐	☐		dip	☐	☐
12	on	☐	☐	**9**	fat	☐	☐
	mom	☐	☐		fan	☐	☐
	top	☐	☐		if	☐	☐
	not	☐	☐		fit	☐	☐
11	has	☐	☐	**8**	cat	☐	☐
	hats	☐	☐		can	☐	☐
	him	☐	☐		sick	☐	☐
	hid	☐	☐		pack	☐	☐

Number Correct (accuracy): _____ /24

Number Automatic (fluency): _____ /24

Learn and Blend

Directions: Listen and join in.

b…b…b…
Bounce the ball fast.
b…b…b…
Bounce it slow.

Bb

Blend It

Directions: Chorally say the sounds and read the words.

INTRODUCE

1. b	r	o	a
2. bat	cat	bad	mad
3. bit	sit	rob	rib

REVIEW

4. fan	pick	dad	mom

CHALLENGE

5. bats	cats	sits	hits

IN CONTEXT

6. I see a bat.

7. I see a bat and a ball.

Daily Practice

Directions: Do one activity each day. Then check the box.

☐ Build Fluency Read the words each day by yourself and to a partner.

☐ Mark It Circle all the words with b.

☐ Spell It Have a partner say each word. Write the word. Check your answer.

☐ Write About It Use the words to create a story. Draw a box around words from the list that you used.

Read-Spell-Write

Directions: Write each word two times. Say each letter as you write it.

1. or

2. are

Use in Context

Directions: Complete each sentence with a word from above.
Read the finished sentences to a partner.

1. Is the cat big _____ little?

2. The cats _____ little.

Name _____

Good or Bad?

—

I see big bats.
Good or bad?

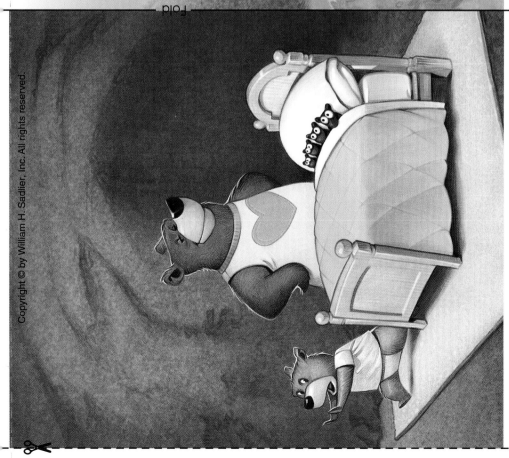

The bats are in my bed!
Good or bad?

4

2

The bats are in the tree.
Good or bad?

The bats are in the cave.
Good or bad?

3

Trace and Write

Directions: Trace and write the letters **B** and **b**. These letters stand for /b/. Say the sound each time you write the letter.

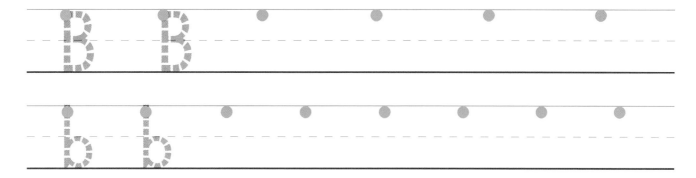

Directions: Say the name of the picture. Write **Bb** on the line if the picture name begins with /b/.

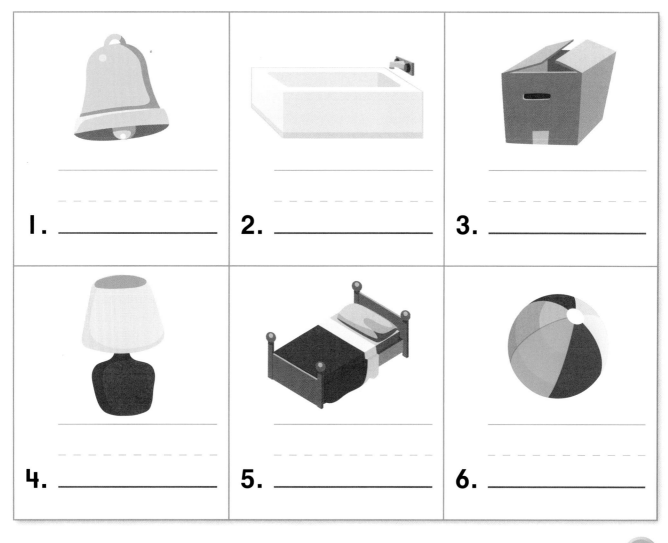

1. _____

2. _____

3. _____

4. _____

5. _____

6. _____

Think and Write

Directions: Listen to each picture name. Write the first letter of the picture name on the line.

1.  _____

2.  _____

Directions: Listen to each picture name. Write the letter for each sound in a separate box.

3.

4.

Listen and Spell

Directions: Write each word and sentence that you hear.

1. _____

2. _____

Trace, Write, and Build

Directions: Trace and write each word.
Then build each word with letter cards.

TRACE	WRITE
or	
are	
bat	
bad	
rat	

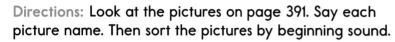

Sort It Out

Directions: Look at the pictures on page 391. Say each picture name. Then sort the pictures by beginning sound.

Bb	Dd

What words do you know with these sounds?

Read and Write

Directions: Say the picture name. Circle the first letter of the picture name.
Write the letter on the line.

b
d
t

1. _____

b
h
p

2. _____

b
c
f

3. _____

b
d
p

4. _____

b
n
p

5. _____

b
d
t

6. _____

Build Fluency

Directions: Complete each sentence with a word from the box.

are   and

1. The cats _____ big.

2. I see Bob _____ Tom.

Directions: Write a sentence using each word.

3. | ran |

4. | bat |

Write About It

Directions: Read "Good or Bad?" again.
Draw a picture about bats. Write about your picture.

Fluency Check

Directions: Listen to the child read the word list. Mark one check in the green box if the word is read correctly (accuracy). Mark another check in the blue box if it is read automatically (fluency).

CUMULATIVE ASSESSMENT									
Lesson	Word			Lesson	Word				
14	bats	☐	☐	11	has	☐	☐		
	bad	☐	☐		hats	☐	☐		
	bit	☐	☐		him	☐	☐		
	rob	☐	☐		hid	☐	☐		
13	ran	☐	☐	10	dad	☐	☐		
	rats	☐	☐		did	☐	☐		
	rip	☐	☐		sad	☐	☐		
	rock	☐	☐		dip	☐	☐		
12	on	☐	☐	9	fat	☐	☐		
	mom	☐	☐		fan	☐	☐		
	top	☐	☐		if	☐	☐		
	not	☐	☐		fit	☐	☐		

Number Correct (accuracy): _____ /24

Number Automatic (fluency): _____ /24

Learn and Blend

Directions: Listen and join in.

l...l...l...
Lick the lemons
and the limes. Ooo!

Ll

Blend It

Directions: Chorally say the sounds and read the words.

INTRODUCE

1. l	b	o	i
2. lot	hot	hill	fill
3. lap	lip	lid	lit

REVIEW

4. bad	ran	top	his

CHALLENGE

5. lips	hills	bills	bats

IN CONTEXT

6. Bill has a lot.

7. The hill is big.

Daily Practice

Directions: Do one activity each day. Then check the box.

☐ **Build Fluency** Read the words each day by yourself and to a partner.

☐ **Mark It** Circle all the words with l.

☐ **Spell It** Have a partner say each word. Write the word. Check your answer.

☐ **Write About It** Use the words to create a story. Draw a box around words from the list that you used.

Read-Spell-Write

Directions: Write each word two times. Say each letter as you write it.

1. up _____

2. down _____

Use in Context

Directions: Complete each sentence with a word from above.
Read the finished sentences to a partner.

1. Pick _____ the cat.

2. Sit _____ on the mat.

Name _____

Up and Down

Bill ran up the hill.
He had to fill his pail.

1

— Fold —

Bill ran up the hill.
Up. Up. Up!

4

2

Bill ran down the hill.

Down. Down.

D O W N!

Oh, no!

No water.

What did Bill do?

3

Trace and Write

Directions: Trace and write the letters L and l. These letters stand for /l/. Say the sound each time you write the letter.

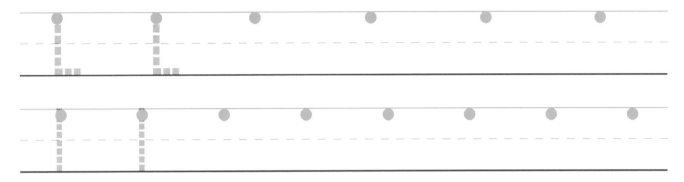

Directions: Say the name of the picture. Write Ll on the line if the picture name begins with /l/.

1. _____

2. _____

3. _____

4. _____

5. _____

6. _____

Think and Write

Directions: Listen to each picture name. Write the first letter of the picture name on the line.

1. 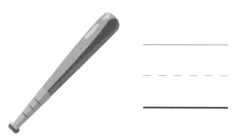 _____

2.  _____

Directions: Listen to each picture name. Write the letter for each sound in a separate box.

3.

4.

Listen and Spell

Directions: Write each word and sentence that you hear.

1. _____

2. _____

Trace, Write, and Build

Directions: Trace and write each word.
Then build each word with letter cards.

TRACE	WRITE
up	
down	
lot	
fill	
hill	

Sort It Out

Directions: Look at the pictures on page 391. Say each picture name. Then sort the pictures by beginning sound.

Ll	Rr

What words do you know with these sounds?

Read and Write

Directions: Say the picture name. Circle the first letter of the picture name.
Write the letter on the line.

m
n
t

1. _____

f
l
r

2. _____

d
l
r

3. _____

b
d
r

4. _____

h
l
t

5. _____

d
f
l

6. _____

Build Fluency

Directions: Complete each sentence with a word from the box.

or	up

1. Sam ran _____ the hill.

2. Is the fan on _____ off?

Directions: Write a sentence using each word.

3. lid _____

_____

4. bad _____

_____

Write About It

Directions: Read "Up and Down" again. Draw a picture about Bill. Write about your picture.

Fluency Check

Directions: Listen to the child read the list below. Mark one check in the green box if the word is read correctly (accuracy). Mark another check in the blue box if it is read automatically (fluency).

CUMULATIVE ASSESSMENT							
Lesson	Word			Lesson	Word		
15	lips	☐	☐	12	on	☐	☐
	lid	☐	☐		mom	☐	☐
	lot	☐	☐		top	☐	☐
	fill	☐	☐		not	☐	☐
14	bats	☐	☐	11	has	☐	☐
	bad	☐	☐		hats	☐	☐
	bit	☐	☐		him	☐	☐
	rob	☐	☐		hid	☐	☐
13	ran	☐	☐	10	dad	☐	☐
	rats	☐	☐		did	☐	☐
	rip	☐	☐		sad	☐	☐
	rock	☐	☐		dip	☐	☐

Number Correct (accuracy): _____ /24

Number Automatic (fluency): _____ /24

Dear Family,

Home Connection

In this unit, your child will learn about words that contain short vowel **e**. He or she will learn to read words with the short vowel **e, k, g, w,** and **x** sounds, such as **hen; sock; dog; wag;** and **fox**.

Read Connected Text

For each week's lesson, your child will read a Take-Home Book that focuses on the lesson skill. At week's end, the book will be sent home with your child. Read the book to your child, or read it aloud together, pointing to each word as you say it. Multiple readings will give your child practice with the lesson skill.

Practice with the Take-Home Book

Ask your child to point to words in the story that include the vowel or consonant sound for that lesson.

Have your child tell you about the book in one sentence. Write what your child says and read the description aloud together.

Lesson Skills and Take-Home Books

Lesson 16 **Kk:** "Run, Kim!"
Lesson 17 **Short e:** "Ten Little Men"
Lesson 18 **Gg:** "Where Am I?"
Lesson 19 **Ww:** "We Will Win!"
Lesson 20 **Xx:** "Six Boxes"

Extend the Learning

With your child, look for words with short vowel **e** in books, signs, magazine covers, etc. Keep a notebook of words you discover.

Challenge your child to identify objects in your home or other locations that have a short vowel **e** sound. For example, "I spy a pen."

 Visit SadlierConnect.com for Student & Family Resources.

Apreciada familia:

En esta unidad, su niño(a) aprenderá palabras que contengan la vocal **e**. Aprenderá a leer palabras con el sonido corto de la **e**, y los sonidos de la **k**, de la **g**, de la **w** y de la **x**, tales como **hen; sock; dog; wag** y **fox**.

Leyendo la historieta en el Take-Home Book

Para cada lección de la semana su niño(a) leerá un cuadernillo de historietas, Take-Home Book, que se enfoca en las destrezas de la lección. Al final de cada semana su niño(a) llevará el cuadernillo a la casa. Lea la historieta a su niño(a) o leánla en voz alta juntos, señalando cada palabra al decirla. Leer varias veces ayudará a su niño(a) a practicar las destrezas de la lección.

Practicando con el Take-Home Book

Pida a su niño(a) señalar en la historieta palabras que incluyan el sonido de la vocal o de la consonante para esa lección. Luego pídale que resuma la historieta en una frase. Escriba lo que dice su niño(a) y después lean juntos lo que escribió.

Lesson Skills and Take-Home Books

Lesson 16 **Kk:** "Run, Kim!"
Lesson 17 **Short e:** "Ten Little Men"
Lesson 18 **Gg:** "Where Am I?"
Lesson 19 **Ww:** "We Will Win!"
Lesson 20 **Xx:** "Six Boxes"

Ampliando el aprendizaje

Con su niño(a) busque palabras con vocales con sonido corto de la **e** en libros, letreros, portadas de revistas, etc. Haga una libreta con palabras que descubran juntos.

Rete a su niño(a) a identificar, ya sea en su casa o en otros lugares, objetos que tengan el sonido corto de la vocal **e**. Por ejemplo: "I spy a pen."

 Visite SadlierConnect.com **para recursos para el estudiante y la familia.**

Learn and Blend

Directions: Listen and join in.

k…k…k…
Kick that ball!

Kk

Blend It

Directions: Chorally say the sounds and read the words.

INTRODUCE

1. k	l	o	a
2. kick	sick	lock	rock

REVIEW

3. kid	kiss	sock	sack
4. lid	fill	bad	rip

CHALLENGE

5. sacks	socks	packs	kids

IN CONTEXT

6. Did you kick it?

7. Kim is a kid.

Daily Practice

Directions: Do one activity each day. Then check the box.

☐ **Build Fluency** Read the words each day by yourself and to a partner.

☐ **Mark It** Circle all the words with k.

☐ **Spell It** Have a partner say each word. Write the word. Check your answer.

☐ **Write About It** Use the words to create a story. Draw a box around words from the list that you used.

Read-Spell-Write

Directions: Write each word two times. Say each letter as you write it.

1. she _____

2. her _____

Use in Context

Directions: Complete each sentence with a word from above.
Read the finished sentences to a partner.

1. _____ has a hat.

2. Is this _____ sock?

Name _____

Run, Kim!

1

Kim picks up her ball.

She packs it in her bag.

Kick it in the goal.

Kim! You rock!

4

2

She looks under her bed.

She sees her socks.

She will kiss her mom.

Tick-tock! Run, Kim!

3

Trace and Write

Directions: Trace and write the letters K and k. These letters stand for /k/. Say the sound each time you write the letter.

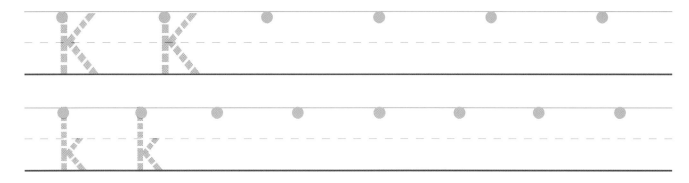

Directions: Say the name of the picture. Write Kk on the line if the picture name begins with /k/.

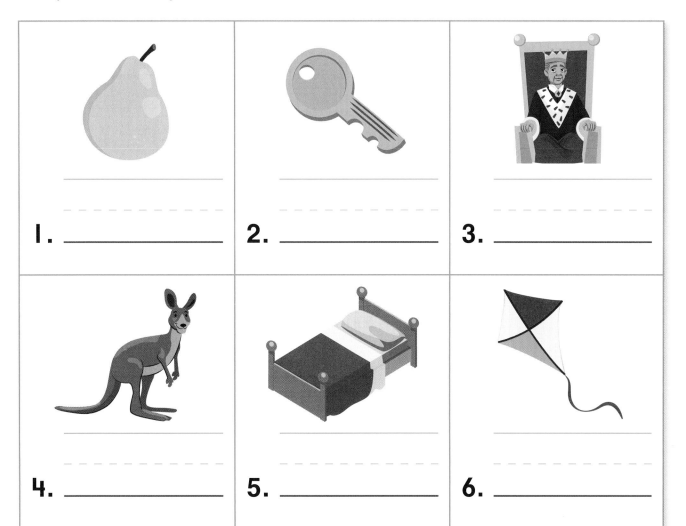

1. _____

2. _____

3. _____

4. _____

5. _____

6. _____

Think and Write

Directions: Listen to each picture name. Write the first letter of the picture name on the line.

1.
_____

2.
_____

Directions: Listen to each picture name. Write the letter for each sound in a separate box.

3.

4.

Listen and Spell

Directions: Write each word and sentence that you hear.

1. _____

_____

2. _____

Trace, Write, and Build

Directions: Trace and write each word.
Then build each word with letter cards.

TRACE	WRITE
she	
her	
kid	
kick	
back	

Sort It Out

Directions: Look at the pictures on page 393. Say each picture name. Then sort the pictures by beginning sound.

Hh

Kk

What words do you know with these sounds?

_____

- -

_____

- -

_____

Read and Write

Directions: Say the picture name. Circle the first letter of the picture name.
Write the letter on the line.

l
n
p

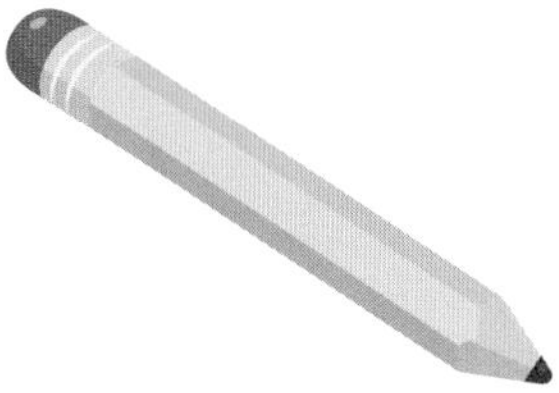

1. _____

h
k
r

2. _____

d
h
k

3. _____

k
r
t

4. _____

d
k
s

5. _____

k
p
t

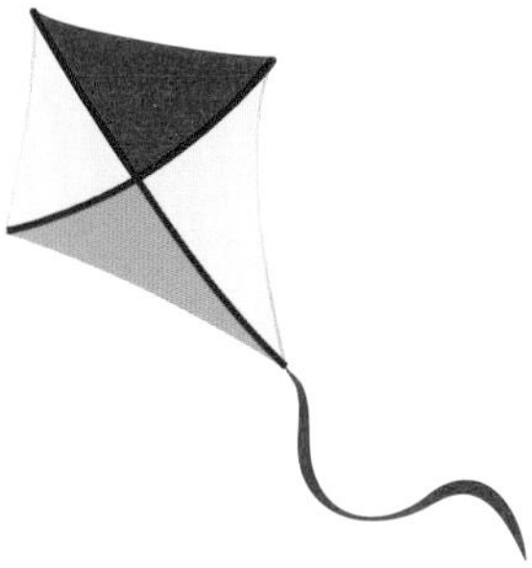

6. _____

Build Fluency

Directions: Complete each sentence with a word from the box.

down	she

1. I can hop up and _____.

2. _____ is my mom.

Directions: Write a sentence using each word.

3. kid _____

_____

4. lap _____

_____

Write About It

Directions: Read "Run, Kim!" again. Draw a picture about Kim. Write about your picture.

Fluency Check

Directions: Listen to the child read the word list. Mark one check in the green box if the word is read correctly (accuracy). Mark another check in the blue box if it is read automatically (fluency).

CUMULATIVE ASSESSMENT							
Lesson	Word			Lesson	Word		
16	kid	☐	☐	13	ran	☐	☐
	kiss	☐	☐		rats	☐	☐
	kick	☐	☐		rip	☐	☐
	lock	☐	☐		rock	☐	☐
15	lips	☐	☐	12	on	☐	☐
	lid	☐	☐		mom	☐	☐
	lot	☐	☐		top	☐	☐
	fill	☐	☐		not	☐	☐
14	bats	☐	☐	11	has	☐	☐
	bad	☐	☐		hats	☐	☐
	bit	☐	☐		him	☐	☐
	rob	☐	☐		hid	☐	☐

Number Correct (accuracy): _____ /24

Number Automatic (fluency): _____ /24

Learn and Blend

Directions: Listen and join in.

e…e…e…
Slowly goes the
engine up the hill.

Ee

Blend It

Directions: Chorally say the sounds and read the words.

INTRODUCE

1. e	a	i	o
2. men	ten	met	set
3. sell	tell	red	fed

REVIEW

4. kick	lot	bat	map

CHALLENGE

5. pens	hens	bells	pets

IN CONTEXT

6. Ed has ten hats.

7. Ben fell on the rock.

Daily Practice

Directions: Do one activity each day. Then check the box.

☐ **Build Fluency** Read the words each day by yourself and to a partner.

☐ **Mark It** Circle all the words with en.

☐ **Spell It** Have a partner say each word. Write the word. Check your answer.

☐ **Write About It** Use the words to create a story. Draw a box around words from the list that you used.

Read-Spell-Write

Directions: Write each word two times. Say each letter as you write it.

1. make _____

2. they _____

Use in Context

Directions: Complete each sentence with a word from above.
Read the finished sentences to a partner.

1. _____ sit on the mat.

2. I can _____ my bed.

—

Ten Little Men

Name _____

Ten little men eat.
They make a big mess.

Ten little men stop.
They hop in ten little beds.

4

2

Ten little men work.
They make a big house.

The bell rings!
Ten little men look up.

3

Trace and Write

Directions: Trace and write the letters **E** and **e**. These letters stand for /e/. Say the sound each time you write the letter.

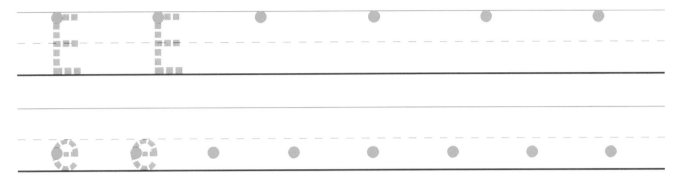

Directions: Say the name of the picture. Write **Ee** on the line if the picture name has the short e sound.

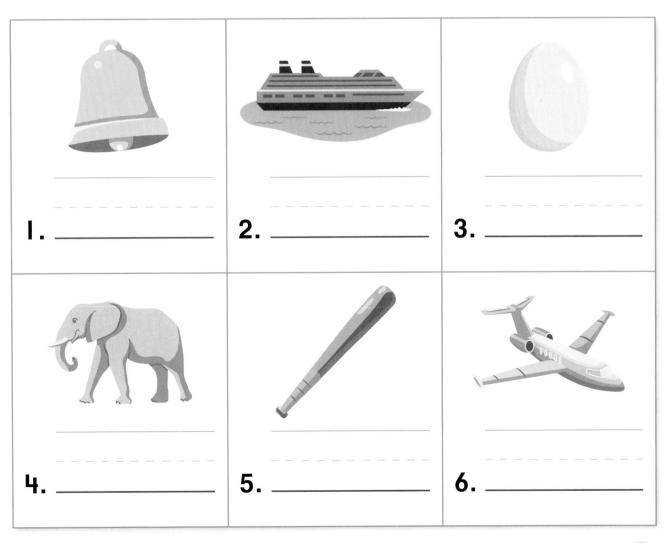

1. _____

2. _____

3. _____

4. _____

5. _____

6. _____

Think and Write

Directions: Listen to each picture name. Write the first letter of the picture name on the line.

1.  _____

2.  _____

Directions: Listen to each picture name. Write the letter for each sound in a separate box.

3.

4.

Listen and Spell

Directions: Write each word and sentence that you hear.

1. _____

2. _____

Trace, Write, and Build

Directions: Trace and write each word.
Then build each word with letter cards.

TRACE	WRITE
make	
they	
men	
ten	
red	

Sort It Out

Directions: Look at the pictures on page 393. Say each picture name.
Then sort the pictures by the vowel sound you hear.

Short e	Short i

What words do you know with these sounds?

Read and Write

Directions: Say the picture name. Circle the letter for the vowel sound you hear. Write the letter on the line.

a
e
i

1. _____

a
e
i

2. _____

a
i
o

3. _____

e
i
o

4. _____

a
e
i

5. _____

a
e
i

6. _____

Build Fluency

Directions: Complete each sentence with a word from the box.

her   make

1. This is _____ sock.

2. I can _____ a map.

Directions: Write a sentence using each word.

3. | pet | _____

_____

4. | sick | _____

_____

Write About It

Directions: Read "Ten Little Men" again. Draw a picture about the ten little men. Write about your picture.

Fluency Check

Directions: Listen to the child read the list below. Mark one check in the green box if the word is read correctly (accuracy). Mark another check in the blue box if it is read automatically (fluency).

CUMULATIVE ASSESSMENT							
Lesson	Word			Lesson	Word		
17	men	☐	☐	14	bats	☐	☐
	sell	☐	☐		bad	☐	☐
	red	☐	☐		bit	☐	☐
	let	☐	☐		rob	☐	☐
16	kid	☐	☐	13	ran	☐	☐
	kiss	☐	☐		rats	☐	☐
	kick	☐	☐		rip	☐	☐
	lock	☐	☐		rock	☐	☐
15	lips	☐	☐	12	on	☐	☐
	lid	☐	☐		mom	☐	☐
	lot	☐	☐		top	☐	☐
	fill	☐	☐		not	☐	☐

Number Correct (accuracy): _____ /24

Numbuer Automatic (fluency): _____ /24

Learn and Blend

Directions: Listen and join in.

g…g…g…
Gulp the grape juice.
So good!

Gg

Blend It

Directions: Chorally say the sounds and read the words.

INTRODUCE

1. g	k	e	i
2. leg	beg	big	pig
3. dig	dog	bag	rag

REVIEW

4. egg	mess	kid	bill

CHALLENGE

5. legs	eggs	dogs	pigs

IN CONTEXT

6. Meg has a red egg.

7. The dog is big!

Daily Practice

Directions: Do one activity each day. Then check the box.

☐ Build Fluency Read the words each day by yourself and to a partner.

☐ Mark It Circle all the words with g.

☐ Spell It Have a partner say each word. Write the word. Check your answer.

☐ Write About It Use the words to create a story. Draw a box around words from the list that you used.

Read-Spell-Write

Directions: Write each word two times. Say each letter as you write it.

1. where _____

2. with _____

Use in Context

Directions: Complete each sentence with a word from above.
Read the finished sentences to a partner.

1. _____ are you?

2. I am _____ Ben.

Name _____

Where Am I?

Fold

I see a hen.

I see a nest with eggs.

Where am I?

—

I see a log.

I dig a big hole.

Where am I?

4

2

I see a big cat!

It is in a den.

Where am I?

3

I see a little dog.

It is with a man.

Where am I?

Trace and Write

Directions: Trace and write the letters **G** and **g**. These letters stand for /g/. Say the sound each time you write the letter.

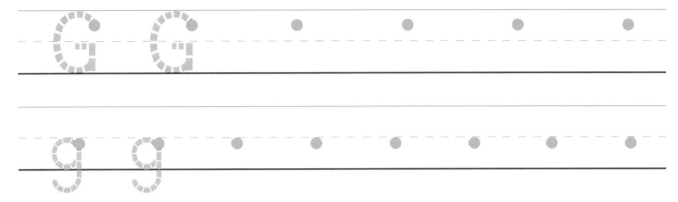

Directions: Say the name of the picture. Write **Gg** on the line if the picture name begins with /g/.

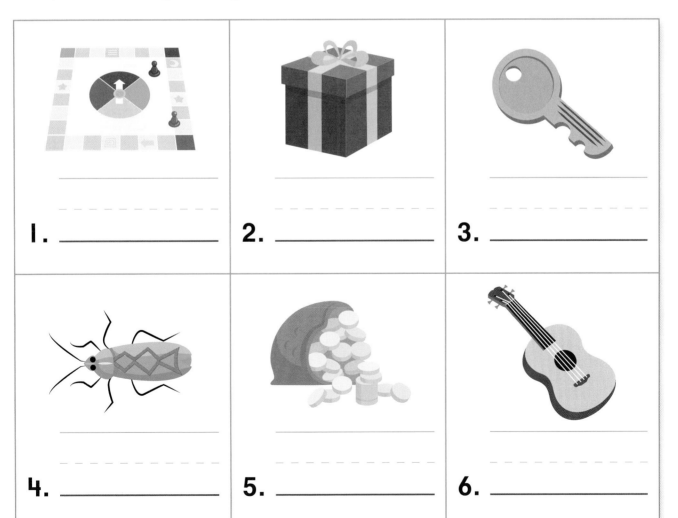

1. _____

2. _____

3. _____

4. _____

5. _____

6. _____

Think and Write

Directions: Listen to each picture name. Write the first letter of the picture name on the line.

1.  _ _ _ _ _ _

2.  _ _ _ _ _ _

Directions: Listen to each picture name. Write the letter for each sound in a separate box.

3.

4.

Listen and Spell

Directions: Write each word and sentence that you hear.

1. _____

2. _____

Trace, Write, and Build

Directions: Trace and write each word.
Then build each word with letter cards.

TRACE	WRITE
where	
with	
leg	
big	
dog	

Sort It Out

Directions: Look at the pictures on page 393. Say each picture name. Then sort the pictures by beginning sound.

Gg	Kk

What words do you know with these sounds?

Read and Write

Directions: Say the picture name. Circle the first letter of the picture name.
Write the letter on the line.

d
f
g

1. _____

b
d
r

2. _____

d
g
p

3. _____

b
d
g

4. _____

d
g
l

5. _____

g
k
t

6. _____

Build Fluency

Directions: Complete each sentence with a word from the box.

they   where

1. _____ is the cat?

2. _____ sit on a rock.

Directions: Write a sentence using each word.

3. big _____

_____

4. pen _____

_____

Write About It

Directions: Read "Where Am I?" again. Draw a picture that shows one place the girl goes. Write about your picture.

Fluency Check

Directions: Listen to the child read the list below. Mark one check in the green box if the word is read correctly (accuracy). Mark another check in the blue box if it is read automatically (fluency).

CUMULATIVE ASSESSMENT							
Lesson	Word			Lesson	Word		
18	eggs	☐	☐	**15**	lips	☐	☐
	got	☐	☐		lid	☐	☐
	pig	☐	☐		lot	☐	☐
	log	☐	☐		fill	☐	☐
17	men	☐	☐	**14**	bats	☐	☐
	sell	☐	☐		bad	☐	☐
	red	☐	☐		bit	☐	☐
	let	☐	☐		rob	☐	☐
16	kid	☐	☐	**13**	ran	☐	☐
	kiss	☐	☐		rats	☐	☐
	kick	☐	☐		rip	☐	☐
	lock	☐	☐		rock	☐	☐

Number Correct (accuracy): _____ /24

Number Automatic (fluency): _____ /24

Learn and Blend

Directions: Listen and join in.

w…w…w…
Wash the windows.

Ww

Blend It

Directions: Chorally say the sounds and read the words.

INTRODUCE

1. w	g	e	o
2. will	fill	win	pin

REVIEW

3. wig	wag	bag	big
4. log	red	lid	cap

CHALLENGE

5. dogs	beds	lips	wins

IN CONTEXT

6. I will get a pet dog.

7. Did you win?

Daily Practice

Directions: Do one activity each day. Then check the box.

☐ Build Fluency Read the words each day by yourself and to a partner.

☐ Mark It Circle all the words with w.

☐ Spell It Have a partner say each word. Write the word. Check your answer.

☐ Write About It Use the words to create a story. Draw a box around words from the list that you used.

Read-Spell-Write

Directions: Write each word two times. Say each letter as you write it.

1. we _____

2. play _____

Use in Context

Directions: Complete each sentence with a word from above.
Read the finished sentences to a partner.

1. I will _____ with you.

2. _____ get wet.

Name _____

We Will Win!

1

I am Dan.

This is Ben.

We like basketball.

Yes. We will win!

4

2

We play it a lot.
We play it well.

We play with friends.
Will we win?

3

Trace and Write

Directions: Trace and write the letters W and w. These letters stand for /w/. Say the sound each time you write the letter.

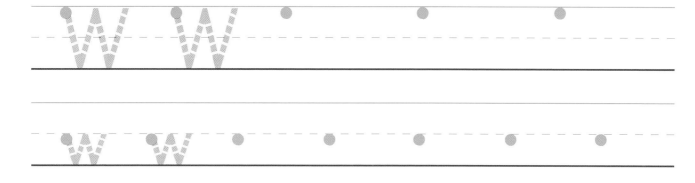

Directions: Say the name of the picture. Write Ww on the line if the picture name begins with /w/.

1. _____

2. _____

3. _____

4. _____

5. _____

6. _____

Think and Write

Directions: Listen to each picture name. Write the first letter of the picture name on the line.

1.  _____

2.  _____

Directions: Listen to each picture name. Write the letter for each sound in a separate box.

3.

4.

Listen and Spell

Directions: Write each word and sentence that you hear.

1. _____

2. _____

Trace, Write, and Build

Directions: Trace and write each word.
Then build each word with letter cards.

TRACE	WRITE
we	
play	
will	
win	
wag	

Sort It Out

Directions: Look at the pictures on page 393. Say each picture name. Then sort the pictures by beginning sound.

Hh	Ww

What words do you know with these sounds?

Read and Write

Directions: Say the picture name. Circle the first letter of the picture name.
Write the letter on the line.

1.
h
t
w

2.
b
h
w

3.
k
n
w

4.
p
t
w

5.
d
h
w

6.
f
m
w

Build Fluency

Directions: Complete each sentence with a word from the box.

with	we

1. I am _____ my dad.

2. _____ fed the hen.

Directions: Write a sentence using each word.

3. | win |
_____
_____

4. | bag |
_____
_____

Write About It

Directions: Read "We Will Win!" again. Draw a picture that shows what Dan and Ben do. Write about your picture.

Fluency Check

Directions: Listen to the child read the list below. Mark one check in the green box if the word is read correctly (accuracy). Mark another check in the blue box if it is read automatically (fluency).

CUMULATIVE ASSESSMENT							
Lesson	**Word**			**Lesson**	**Word**		
19	win	☐	☐	**16**	kid	☐	☐
	will	☐	☐		kiss	☐	☐
	wigs	☐	☐		kick	☐	☐
	wag	☐	☐		lock	☐	☐
18	eggs	☐	☐	**15**	lips	☐	☐
	got	☐	☐		lid	☐	☐
	pig	☐	☐		lot	☐	☐
	log	☐	☐		fill	☐	☐
17	men	☐	☐	**14**	bats	☐	☐
	sell	☐	☐		bad	☐	☐
	red	☐	☐		bit	☐	☐
	let	☐	☐		rob	☐	☐

Number Correct (accuracy): _____ /24

Number Automatic (fluency): _____ /24

Learn and Blend

Directions: Listen and join in.

x...x...x...
Mix the batter.

Xx

Blend It

Directions: Chorally say the sounds and read the words.

INTRODUCE

1. x	w	g	e
2. ax	ox	box	socks
3. fox	fix	mix	six

REVIEW

4. will	pig	bell	not

CHALLENGE

5. boxes	foxes	mixes	fixes

IN CONTEXT

6. Can you fix it?

7. I see a red fox.

Daily Practice

Directions: Do one activity each day. Then check the box.

☐ **Build Fluency** Read the words each day by yourself and to a partner.

☐ **Mark It** Circle all the words with x.

☐ **Spell It** Have a partner say each word. Write the word. Check your answer.

☐ **Write About It** Use the words to create a story. Draw a box around words from the list that you used.

Read-Spell-Write

Directions: Write each word two times. Say each letter as you write it.

1. one _____

2. have _____

Use in Context

Directions: Complete each sentence with a word from above.
Read the finished sentences to a partner.

1. Max has _____ red pen.

2. I _____ a pet.

Name _____

Six Boxes

Max has six boxes.
Six big boxes!

Yes. Max can fix it.
He has six good boxes.

—

4

2

Two boxes have foxes.

Three boxes have books.

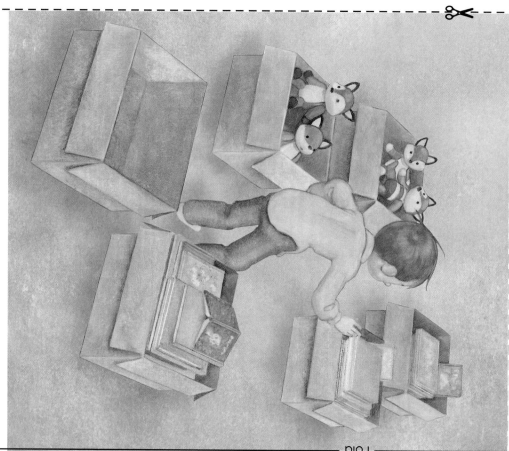

One box has a rip.

Can Max fix it?

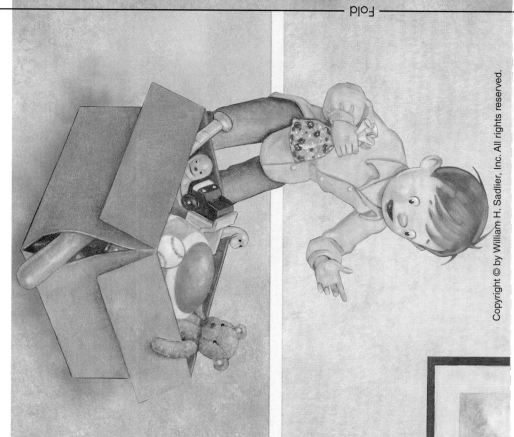

3

Trace and Write

Directions: Trace and write the letters **X** and **x**. These letters stand for /ks/. Say the sound each time you write the letter.

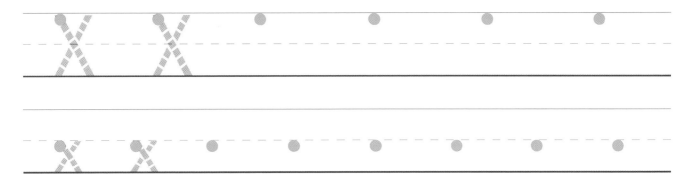

Directions: Say the name of the picture. Write Xx on the line if the picture name ends with /ks/.

1. _____

2. _____

3. _____

4. _____

5. _____

6. _____

Think and Write

Directions: Listen to each picture name. Write the first letter of the picture name on the line.

1.  _____

2.  _____

Directions: Listen to each picture name. Write the letter for each sound in a separate box.

3.

4.

Listen and Spell

Directions: Write each word and sentence that you hear.

1. _____

2. _____

Trace, Write, and Build

Directions: Trace and write each word.
Then build each word with letter cards.

TRACE	WRITE
one	
have	
box	
fix	
six	

Sort It Out

Directions: Look at the pictures on page 393. Say each picture name. Then sort the pictures by ending sound.

Gg	Xx

What words do you know with these sounds?

Read and Write

Directions: Say the picture name. Circle the last letter of the picture name.
Write the letter on the line.

p
t
x

1. _____

b
t
x

2. _____

k
s
x

3. _____

h
p
t

4. _____

s
t
x

5. _____

t
w
x

6. _____

Build Fluency

Directions: Complete each sentence with a word from the box.

one	play

1. I will _____ with you.

2. Ron has _____ egg.

Directions: Write a sentence using each word.

3. box _____

_____

4. well _____

_____

Write About It

Directions: Read "Six Boxes" again. Draw a picture that shows Max's boxes. Write about your picture.

Fluency Check

Directions: Listen to the child read the list below. Mark one check in the green box if the word is read correctly (accuracy). Mark another check in the blue box if it is read automatically (fluency).

CUMULATIVE ASSESSMENT							
Lesson	Word			Lesson	Word		
20	ax	☐	☐	17	men	☐	☐
	fox	☐	☐		sell	☐	☐
	boxes	☐	☐		red	☐	☐
	six	☐	☐		let	☐	☐
19	win	☐	☐	16	kid	☐	☐
	will	☐	☐		kiss	☐	☐
	wigs	☐	☐		kick	☐	☐
	wag	☐	☐		lock	☐	☐
18	eggs	☐	☐	15	lips	☐	☐
	got	☐	☐		lid	☐	☐
	pig	☐	☐		lot	☐	☐
	log	☐	☐		fill	☐	☐

Number Correct (accuracy): _____ /24

Number Automatic (fluency): _____ /24

Dear Family,

In this unit, your child will learn about words that contain the short vowel **u**. He or she will learn to read words with the short vowel **u, v, j, q,** and **y** sounds, such as **suds; vet; jug; quit;** and **yell**.

Read Connected Text

For each week's lesson, your child will read a Take-Home Book that focuses on the lesson skill. At week's end, the book will be sent home with your child. Read the book to your child, or read it aloud together, pointing to each word as you say it. Multiple readings will give your child practice with the lesson skill.

Practice with the Take-Home Book

Ask your child to point to words in the story that include the vowel or consonant sound for that lesson.

Have your child tell you about the book in one sentence. Write what your child says and read the description aloud together.

Lesson Skills and Take-Home Books

Lesson 21 **Vv:** "The Best Vet"
Lesson 22 **Short u:** "The Bus"
Lesson 23 **Jj:** "What Will Jan Do?"
Lesson 24 **Qu:** "Quick, Quick, Quick!"
Lesson 25 **Yy:** "Yes!"

Extend the Learning

With your child, look for words with short vowel **u** in books, signs, magazine covers, etc. Keep a notebook of words you discover.

Challenge your child to identify objects in your home or other locations that have a short vowel **u** sound. For example, "I spy a duck."

 Visit SadlierConnect.com **for Student & Family Resources.**

Apreciada familia:

En esta unidad, su niño(a) aprenderá palabras que contienen la vocal **u**. Aprenderá a leer palabras con el sonido corto de la **u**, y los sonidos de la **v**, de la **j**, de la **q** y de la **y**, tales como **suds; vet; jug; quit** y **yell**.

Leyendo la historieta en el Take-Home Book

Para cada lección de la semana su niño(a) leerá un cuadernillo de historietas, Take-Home Book, que se enfoca en las destrezas de la lección. Al final de cada semana su niño(a) llevará el cuadernillo a la casa. Lea la historieta a su niño(a) o léanla en voz alta juntos, señalando cada palabra al decirla. Leer varias veces ayudará a su niño(a) a practicar las destrezas de la lección.

Practicando con el Take-Home Book

Pida a su niño(a) señalar en la historieta palabras que incluyan el sonido de la vocal o de la consonante para esa lección. Luego pídale que resuma la historieta en una frase. Escriba lo que dice su niño(a) y después lean juntos lo que escribió.

Lesson Skills and Take-Home Books

Lesson 21 **Vv:** "The Best Vet"

Lesson 22 **Short u:** "The Bus"

Lesson 23 **Jj:** "What Will Jan Do?"

Lesson 24 **Qu:** "Quick, Quick, Quick!"

Lesson 25 **Yy:** "Yes!"

Ampliando el aprendizaje

Con su niño(a) busque palabras con vocales con sonido corto de la **u** en libros, letreros, portadas de revistas, etc. Haga una libreta con palabras que descubran juntos.

Rete a su niño(a) a identificar, ya sea en su casa o en otros lugares, objetos que tengan el sonido corto de la vocal **u**. Por ejemplo: "I spy a duck."

 Visite **SadlierConnect.com** para recursos para el estudiante y la familia.

Learn and Blend

Directions: Listen and join in.

V...v...v...
Vroom! The vacuum
cleans the rug.

Blend It

Directions: Chorally say the sounds and read the words.

INTRODUCE

1. v   x   g   w

2. van   pan   vet   get

REVIEW

3. top   stop   lip   slip

4. box   wig   men   pack

CHALLENGE

5. smell   spell   stick   snack

IN CONTEXT

6. We have a big van.

7. The vet can help sick pets.

Daily Practice

Directions: Do one activity each day. Then check the box.

☐ Build Fluency Read the words each day by yourself and to a partner.

☐ Mark It Circle all the words with v.

☐ Spell It Have a partner say each word. Write the word. Check your answer.

☐ Write About It Use the words to create a story. Draw a box around words from the list that you used.

Read-Spell-Write

Directions: Write each word two times. Say each letter as you write it.

1. go _____

2. hurt _____

Use in Context

Directions: Complete each sentence with a word from above.
Read the finished sentences to a partner.

1. We will _____ up the hill.

2. I _____ my leg.

Name

The Best Vet

1

Stan's dog is sick.
He will go to the vet.

The vet will help.
She is the best vet!

4

2

The vet will help.
The dog will get well.

Fran's cat is hurt.
She will go to the vet.

3

Trace and Write

Directions: Trace and write the letters V and v. These letters stand for /v/. Say the sound each time you write the letter.

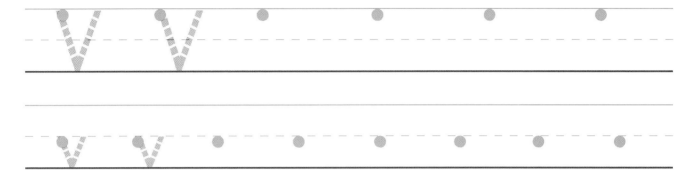

Directions: Say the name of the picture. Write Vv on the line if the picture name begins with /v/.

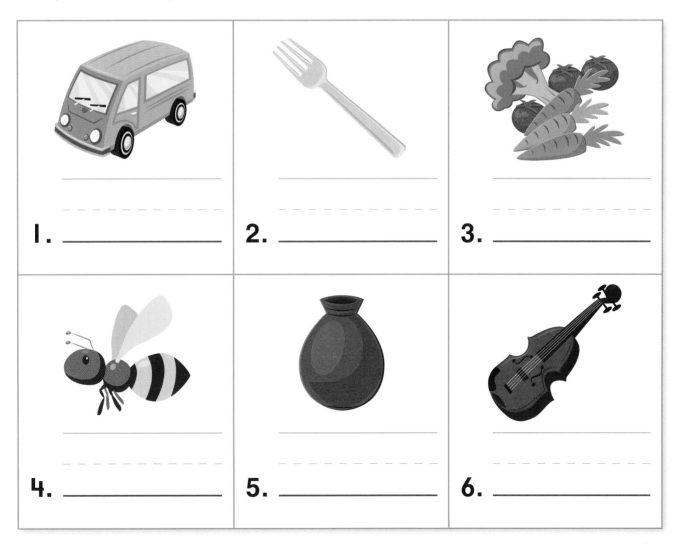

1. _____

2. _____

3. _____

4. _____

5. _____

6. _____

Think and Write

Directions: Listen to each picture name. Write the first letter of the picture name on the line.

1.  _____

2.  _____

Directions: Listen to each picture name. Write the letter for each sound in a separate box.

3.

4.

Listen and Spell

Directions: Write each word and sentence that you hear.

1. _____

_____

2. _____

Trace, Write, and Build

Directions: Trace and write each word.
Then build each word with letter cards.

TRACE	WRITE
go	
hurt	
van	
vet	
get	

Sort It Out

Directions: Look at the pictures on page 395. Say each picture name. Then sort the pictures by beginning sound.

Ff	Vv

What words do you know with these sounds?

_____

_____

_____

_____

Read and Write

Directions: Say the picture name. Circle the first letter of the picture name. Write the letter on the line.

m
v
w

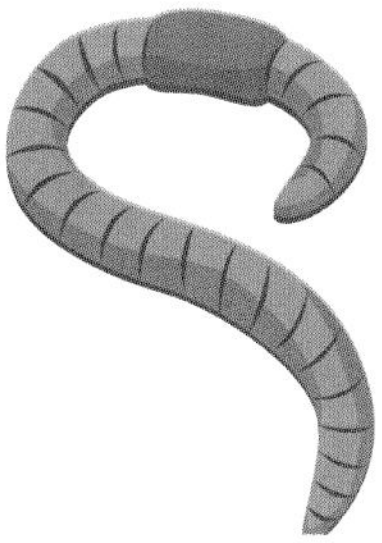

1. _____

f
v
w

2. _____

f
v
w

3. _____

f
h
v

4. _____

t
v
w

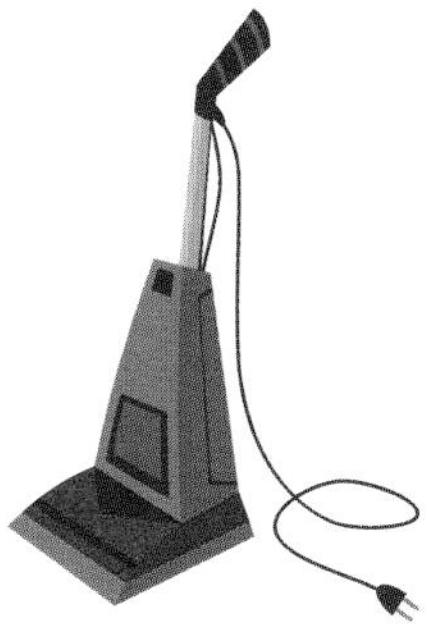

5. _____

l
n
v

6. _____

Build Fluency

Directions: Complete each sentence with a word from the box.

have	go

1. We _____ a pet cat.

2. Where did the cat _____?

Directions: Write a sentence using each word.

3. | van | _____

4. | fix | _____

Write About It

Directions: Read "The Best Vet" again. Draw a picture that shows how the vet helps. Write about your picture.

Fluency Check

Directions: Listen to the child read the list below. Mark one check in the green box if the word is read correctly (accuracy). Mark another check in the blue box if it is read automatically (fluency).

CUMULATIVE ASSESSMENT							
Lesson	**Word**			**Lesson**	**Word**		
21	van	☐	☐	**18**	eggs	☐	☐
	vet	☐	☐		got	☐	☐
	top	☐	☐		pig	☐	☐
	stop	☐	☐		log	☐	☐
20	ax	☐	☐	**17**	men	☐	☐
	fox	☐	☐		sell	☐	☐
	boxes	☐	☐		red	☐	☐
	six	☐	☐		let	☐	☐
19	win	☐	☐	**16**	kid	☐	☐
	will	☐	☐		kiss	☐	☐
	wigs	☐	☐		kick	☐	☐
	wag	☐	☐		lock	☐	☐

Number Correct (accuracy): _____ /24

Number Automatic (fluency): _____ /24

Learn and Blend

Directions: Listen and join in.

U…u…u…
Up goes the umbrella.

Blend It

Directions: Chorally say the sounds and read the words.

INTRODUCE

1. u	o	e	i
2. up	cup	sun	run
3. mud	bus	luck	cut

REVIEW

4. van	six	win	eggs

CHALLENGE

5. bugs	cuts	nuts	ducks

IN CONTEXT

6. Hop on the bus!

7. It is fun to play in the sun.

Daily Practice

Directions: Do one activity each day. Then check the box.

☐ **Build Fluency** Read the words each day by yourself and to a partner.

☐ **Mark It** Circle all the words with un.

☐ **Spell It** Have a partner say each word. Write the word. Check your answer.

☐ **Write About It** Use the words to create a story. Draw a box around words from the list that you used.

Read-Spell-Write

Directions: Write each word two times. Say each letter as you write it.

1. day _____

2. of _____

Use in Context

Directions: Complete each sentence with a word from above.
Read the finished sentences to a partner.

1. Pam had a good _____.

2. I had a lot _____ fun.

1

The Bus

Name _____

Fold

Fold

Ducks hop on the bus.
Ducks will have a day of fun.

But ducks can still have fun.
They can run in the sun.

It is a good day.

4

2

Ducks go up a hill.
But the bus gets stuck in mud.

Fold

Fold

Huff, huff, puff!
Ducks tug on the bus.
What bad luck!

3

Trace and Write

Directions: Trace and write the letters U and u. These letters stand for /u/. Say the sound each time you write the letter.

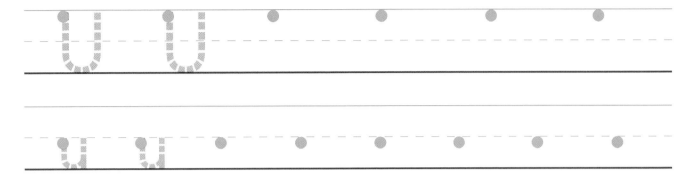

Directions: Say the name of the picture. Write Uu on the line if the picture name has the short u sound.

1. _____ 2. _____ 3. _____

4. _____ 5. _____ 6. _____

Think and Write

Directions: Listen to each picture name. Write the first letter of the picture name on the line.

1. 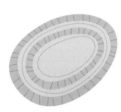 _____

2.  _____

Directions: Listen to each picture name. Write the letter for each sound in a separate box.

3.

4.

Listen and Spell

Directions: Write each word and sentence that you hear.

1. _____

2. _____

Trace, Write, and Build

Directions: Trace and write each word.
Then build each word with letter cards.

TRACE	WRITE
day	
of	
up	
sun	
fun	

Sort It Out

Directions: Look at the pictures on page 395. Say each picture name. Then sort the pictures by the vowel sound you hear.

Short o	Short u

What words do you know with these sounds?

Read and Write

Directions: Say the picture name. Circle the letter for the vowel sound
you hear. Write the letter on the line.

i
o
u

1. _____

a
o
u

2. _____

a
i
u

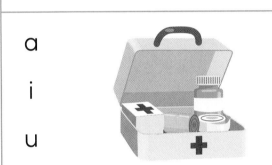

3. _____

e
i
u

4. _____

a
i
u

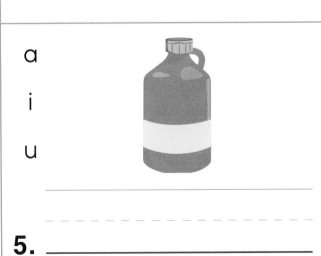

5. _____

i
o
u

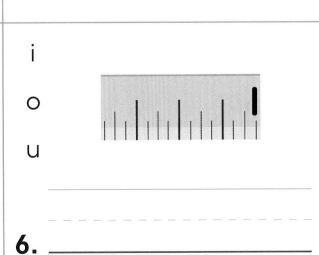

6. _____

Build Fluency

Directions: Complete each sentence with a word from the box.

hurt	day

1. I ran and _____ my leg.

2. Kim had a fun _____.

Directions: Write a sentence using each word.

3. bugs _____

4. vet _____

Write About It

Directions: Read "The Bus" again. Draw a picture that shows what happens to the bus. Write about your picture.

Fluency Check

Directions: Listen to the child read the list below. Mark one check in the green box if the word is read correctly (accuracy). Mark another check in the blue box if it is read automatically (fluency).

CUMULATIVE ASSESSMENT							
Lesson	Word			Lesson	Word		
22	fun	☐	☐	**19**	win	☐	☐
	rub	☐	☐		will	☐	☐
	duck	☐	☐		wigs	☐	☐
	bus	☐	☐		wag	☐	☐
21	van	☐	☐	**18**	eggs	☐	☐
	vet	☐	☐		got	☐	☐
	top	☐	☐		pig	☐	☐
	stop	☐	☐		log	☐	☐
20	ax	☐	☐	**17**	men	☐	☐
	fox	☐	☐		sell	☐	☐
	boxes	☐	☐		red	☐	☐
	six	☐	☐		let	☐	☐

Number Correct (accuracy): _____ /24

Number Automatic (fluency): _____ /24

Learn and Blend

Directions: Listen and join in.

J...j...j...
Jump for joy!

Jj

Blend It

Directions: Chorally say the sounds and read the words.

INTRODUCE

1. j	v	u	e
2. jet	let	jog	dog
3. jam	job	jug	Jill

REVIEW

4. fun	fix	pig	tell

CHALLENGE

5. jets	jogs	jugs	bugs

IN CONTEXT

6. I like to jog.

7. Jill got on the bus.

Daily Practice

Directions: Do one activity each day. Then check the box.

☐ Build Fluency Read the words each day by yourself and to a partner.

☐ Mark It Circle all the words with j.

☐ Spell It Have a partner say each word. Write the word. Check your answer.

☐ Write About It Use the words to create a story. Draw a box around words from the list that you used.

Read-Spell-Write

Directions: Write each word two times. Say each letter as you write it.

1. said _____

2. that _____

Use in Context

Directions: Complete each sentence with a word from above.
Read the finished sentences to a partner.

1. _____ is my van.

2. "No," Jen _____.

—

Name _____

What Will Jan Do?

Fold

"I will jog," said Jan.

Fold

"I will rest," said Jan.
"That is what I will do!"

4

2

"I will hop," said Jan.

"I will jump," said Jan.

3

Trace and Write

Directions: Trace and write the letters **J** and **j**. These letters stand for /j/. Say the sound each time you write the letter.

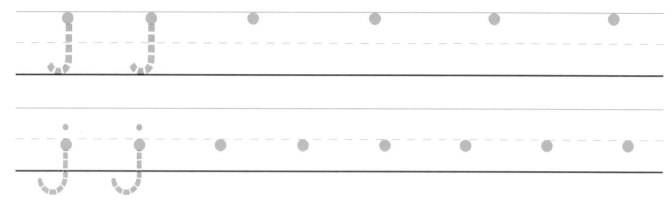

Directions: Say the name of the picture. Write Jj on the line if the picture name begins with the /j/ sound.

1. _____

2. _____

3. _____

4. _____

5. _____

6. _____

Think and Write

Directions: Listen to each picture name. Write the first letter of the picture name on the line.

1.  _____

2.  _____

Directions: Listen to each picture name. Write the letter for each sound in a separate box.

3.

4.

Listen and Spell

Directions: Write each word and sentence that you hear.

1. _____

2. _____

Trace, Write, and Build

Directions: Trace and write each word.
Then build each word with letter cards.

TRACE	WRITE
said	
that	
jet	
job	
jam	

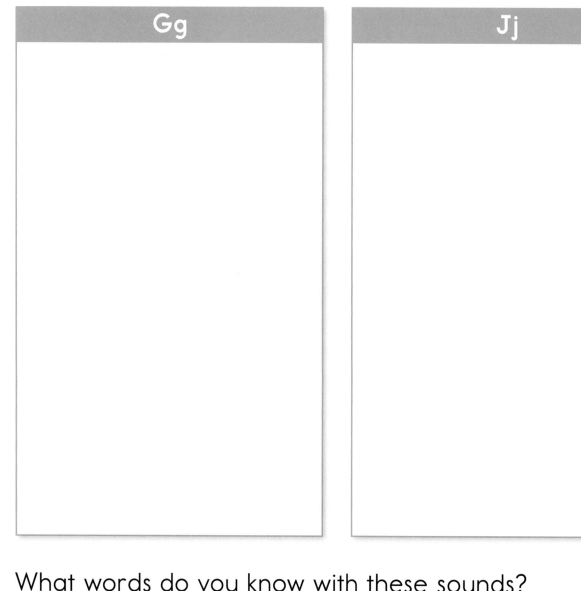

Sort It Out

Directions: Look at the pictures on page 395. Say each picture name. Then sort the pictures by beginning sound.

Gg	Jj

What words do you know with these sounds?

Read and Write

Directions: Say the picture name. Circle the first letter of the picture name. Write the letter on the line.

g
j
t

1. _____

g
h
j

2. _____

j
m
n

3. _____

g
h
j

4. _____

g
j
l

5. _____

j
m
p

6. _____

Build Fluency

Directions: Complete each sentence with a word from the box.

| of said |

1. I sat on top _____ a rock.

2. "I will!" Jan _____ .

Directions: Write a sentence using each word.

3. | jog | _____

4. | bus | _____

Write About It

Directions: Read "What Will Jan Do?" again. Draw a picture that shows one thing that Jan will do. Write about your picture.

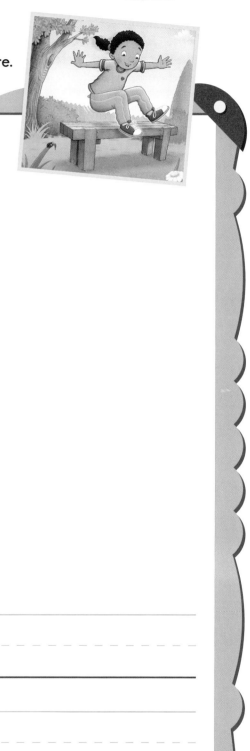

Fluency Check

Directions: Listen to the child read the list below. Mark one check in the green box if the word is read correctly (accuracy). Mark another check in the blue box if it is read automatically (fluency).

Lesson	Word			Lesson	Word		
CUMULATIVE ASSESSMENT							
23	jugs	☐	☐	**20**	ax	☐	☐
	jog	☐	☐		fox	☐	☐
	jet	☐	☐		boxes	☐	☐
	jam	☐	☐		six	☐	☐
22	fun	☐	☐	**19**	win	☐	☐
	rub	☐	☐		will	☐	☐
	duck	☐	☐		wigs	☐	☐
	bus	☐	☐		wag	☐	☐
21	van	☐	☐	**18**	eggs	☐	☐
	vet	☐	☐		got	☐	☐
	top	☐	☐		pig	☐	☐
	stop	☐	☐		log	☐	☐

Number Correct (accuracy): _____ /24

Number Automatic (fluency): _____ /24

Learn and Blend

Directions: Listen and join in.

kw…kw…kw…
Quack quietly like
a little duck.

Qu

Blend It

Directions: Chorally say the sounds and read the words.

INTRODUCE

| **1.** qu | j | v | x |
| **2.** quit | quick | kick | kit |

REVIEW

| **3.** jog | luck | us | van |
| **4.** boxes | win | big | neck |

CHALLENGE

| **5.** led | sled | nap | snap |

IN CONTEXT

6. Jill is quick! She can run fast.

7. Why did you quit?

Daily Practice

Directions: Do one activity each day. Then check the box.

☐ Build Fluency Read the words each day by yourself and to a partner.

☐ Mark It Circle all the words with qu.

☐ Spell It Have a partner say each word. Write the word. Check your answer.

☐ Write About It Use the words to create a story. Draw a box around words from the list that you used.

Read-Spell-Write

Directions: Write each word two times. Say each letter as you write it.

1. there _____

2. out _____

Use in Context

Directions: Complete each sentence with a word from above.
Read the finished sentences to a partner.

1. _____ is my bag.

2. Get _____ of bed!

Name _____

Quick, Quick, Quick!

Run, Hen! Run!

There you go.

Quick, quick, quick!

1

Do not quit.

Do not go back.

Go out!

4

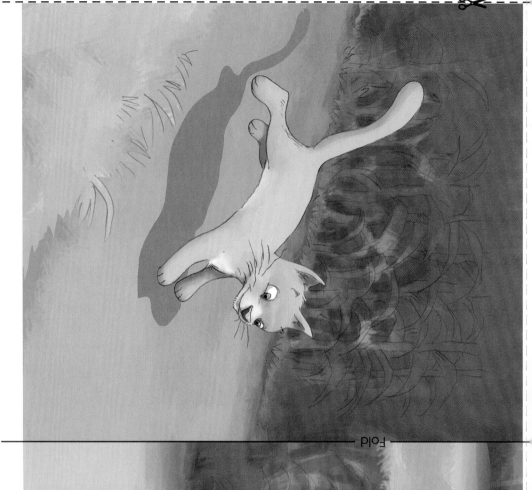

Run, Cat! Run!
There you go.
Quick, quick, quick!

2

Run, Duck! Run!
There you go.
Quack, quack, quack!

3

Trace and Write

Directions: Trace and write the letters Q and q. These letters together with u stand for /kw/. Say the sound each time you write the letter.

Q Q • • • •

q q • • • • • • •

Directions: Say the name of the picture. Write qu on the line if the picture name begins with the /kw/ sound.

1. _____

2. _____

3. _____

4. _____

5. _____

6. _____

Think and Write

Directions: Listen to each picture name. Write the first letter or letters of the picture name on the line.

1.  _____

2.  _____

Directions: Listen to each picture name. Write the letter for each sound in a separate box.

3.

4.

Listen and Spell

Directions: Write each word and sentence that you hear.

1. _____

_____

2. _____

Trace, Write, and Build

Directions: Trace and write each word.
Then build each word with letter cards.

TRACE	WRITE
there	
out	
quit	
quick	
its	

Sort It Out

Directions: Look at the pictures on page 395. Say each picture name. Then sort the pictures by beginning sound.

Qu

Ww

What words do you know with these sounds?

Read and Write

Directions: Say the picture name. Circle the first letter or letters of the picture name. Write the letter or letters on the line.

b

qu

w

1. _____

l

qu

t

2. _____

qu

v

w

3. _____

qu

v

w

4. _____

j

qu

t

5. _____

g

k

qu

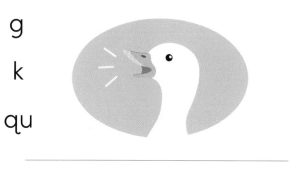

6. _____

Build Fluency

Directions: Complete each sentence with a word from the box.

that out

1. _____ is my hat.

2. Let the dog _____.

Directions: Write a sentence using each word.

3. | quick | _____

_____

4. | jug | _____

_____

Write About It

Directions: Read "Quick, Quick, Quick!" again. Draw a picture about Hen, Cat, and Duck. Write about your picture.

Fluency Check

Directions: Listen to the child read the list below. Mark one check in the green box if the word is read correctly (accuracy). Mark another check in the blue box if it is read automatically (fluency).

CUMULATIVE ASSESSMENT							
Lesson	Word			Lesson	Word		
24	quit	☐	☐	**21**	van	☐	☐
	quick	☐	☐		vet	☐	☐
	kicks	☐	☐		top	☐	☐
	kit	☐	☐		stop	☐	☐
23	jugs	☐	☐	**20**	ax	☐	☐
	jog	☐	☐		fox	☐	☐
	jet	☐	☐		boxes	☐	☐
	jam	☐	☐		six	☐	☐
22	fun	☐	☐	**19**	win	☐	☐
	rub	☐	☐		will	☐	☐
	duck	☐	☐		wigs	☐	☐
	bus	☐	☐		wag	☐	☐

Number Correct (accuracy): _____ /24

Number Automatic (fluency): _____ /24

Learn and Blend

Directions: Listen and join in.

Y…y…y…
Make the yo-yo go
up and down.

Blend It

Directions: Chorally say the sounds and read the words.

INTRODUCE

1. y   qu   j   v

2. yes   yell   sell   tell

3. yum   yet   yap   map

REVIEW

4. quick   jog   sun   leg

CHALLENGE

5. yelling   telling   selling   sticking

IN CONTEXT

6. Do not yell!

7. "Yes!" said Mom. "You can go."

Daily Practice

Directions: Do one activity each day. Then check the box.

☐ Build Fluency Read the words each day by yourself and to a partner.

☐ Mark It Circle all the words with y.

☐ Spell It Have a partner say each word. Write the word. Check your answer.

☐ Write About It Use the words to create a story. Draw a box around words from the list that you used.

Read-Spell-Write

Directions: Write each word two times. Say each letter as you write it.

1. all _____

2. read _____

Use in Context

Directions: Complete each sentence with a word from above.
Read the finished sentences to a partner.

1. We like to _____.

2. We can _____ play.

1

Name

Yes!

Do all kids like to play?

Yes!

Do all dogs like to yip and yap?

Yes! Kids like it as well.

4

2

Do all kids like to read?

Yes!

Fold

Fold

3

Do all kids like to yell?

Yes!

Trace and Write

Directions: Trace and write the letters Y and y. These letters stand for /y/. Say the sound each time you write the letter.

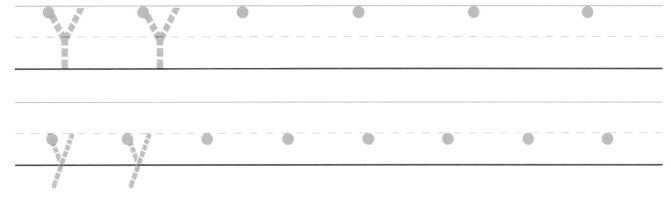

Directions: Say the name of the picture. Write Yy on the line if the picture name begins with the /y/ sound.

1. _____

2. _____

3. _____

4. _____

5. _____

6. _____

Think and Write

Directions: Listen to each picture name. Write the first letter of the picture name on the line.

1.  _____

2.  _____

Directions: Listen to each picture name. Write the letter for each sound in a separate box.

3.

4. **10**

Listen and Spell

Directions: Write each word and sentence that you hear.

1. _____

2. _____

Trace, Write, and Build

Directions: Trace and write each word.
Then build each word with letter cards.

TRACE	WRITE
all	
read	
yes	
yell	
yet	

Sort It Out

Directions: Look at the pictures on page 395. Say each picture name. Then sort the pictures by beginning sound.

Jj	Yy

What words do you know with these sounds?

_____

- -

_____

_____

Read and Write

Directions: Say the picture name. Circle the first letter of the picture name.
Write the letter on the line.

l
w
y

1. _____

j
l
y

2. _____

j
r
y

3. _____

h
w
y

4. _____

j
w
y

5. _____

n
r
y

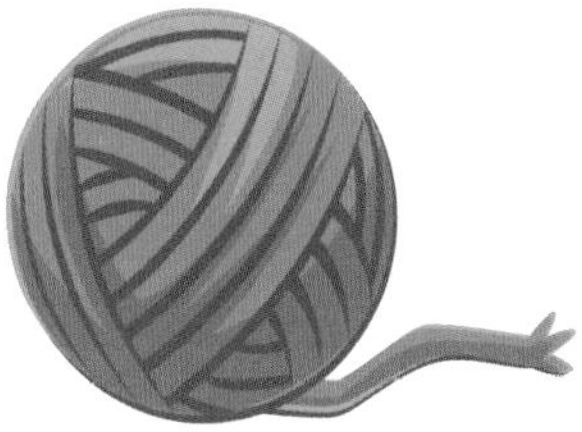

6. _____

Build Fluency

Directions: Complete each sentence with a word from the box.

there   all

_____
- - - - - - - - - - - - - - -

1. You can sit _____.

_____
- - - - - - - - - - - - - - -

2. We _____ like to play.

Directions: Write a sentence using each word.

3. | yet |

4. | quit |

Write About It

Directions: Read "Yes!" again. Draw a picture about something all kids like to do. Write about your picture.

Fluency Check

Directions: Listen to the child read the list below. Mark one check in the green box if the word is read correctly (accuracy). Mark another check in the blue box if it is read automatically (fluency).

CUMULATIVE ASSESSMENT									
Lesson	Word				Lesson	Word			
25	yes	☐	☐		**22**	fun	☐	☐	
	yell	☐	☐			rub	☐	☐	
	yum	☐	☐			duck	☐	☐	
	yap	☐	☐			bus	☐	☐	
24	quit	☐	☐		**21**	van	☐	☐	
	quick	☐	☐			vet	☐	☐	
	kicks	☐	☐			top	☐	☐	
	kit	☐	☐			stop	☐	☐	
23	jugs	☐	☐		**20**	ax	☐	☐	
	jog	☐	☐			fox	☐	☐	
	jet	☐	☐			boxes	☐	☐	
	jam	☐	☐			six	☐	☐	

Number Correct (accuracy): _____ /24

Number Automatic (fluency): _____ /24

Dear Family,

In this unit, your child will learn about words that contain long vowels. He or she will learn to read words with **z**, long vowels in open syllables, and long vowels with final **e**, such as **zip; no; mate; hope;** and **fine**. Your child will also review short vowels.

Read Connected Text

For each week's lesson, your child will read a Take-Home Book that focuses on the lesson skills. At week's end, the book will be sent home with your child. Read the book to your child, or read it aloud together, pointing to each word as you say it. Multiple readings will give your child practice with the lesson skills.

Practice with the Take-Home Book

Ask your child to point to words in the story that include the vowel or consonant sound for that lesson.

Have your child tell you about the book in one sentence. Write what your child says and read the description aloud together.

Lesson Skills and Take-Home Books

Lesson 26 **Zz:** "Zig, Zag, Buzz!"
Lesson 27 **Short Vowel Review:** "Lots of Fun"
Lesson 28 **Single Letter Long Vowels e, i, o:** "We Play"
Lesson 29 **Final e (a_e):** "The Hat"
Lesson 30 **Final e (o_e, i_e):** "The Bike Ride"

Extend the Learning

With your child, look for words with long vowels in books, signs, magazine covers, etc. Keep a notebook of words you discover.

Challenge your child to identify objects in your home or other locations that have a long vowel sound. For example, "I spy a bike."

 Visit **SadlierConnect.com** for Student & Family Resources.

Apreciada familia:

En esta unidad, su niño(a) aprenderá palabras que contienen el sonido largo de las vocales. Aprenderá a leer palabras con la **z**, con vocales con sonido largo con sílabas abiertas, y con vocales con sonido largo y una **e** al final, tales como **zip; no; mate; hope** y **fine**. Su niño(a) también repasará el sonido corto de las vocales.

Leyendo la historieta en el Take-Home Book

Para cada lección de la semana su niño(a) leerá un cuadernillo de historietas, Take-Home Book, que se enfoca en las destrezas de la lección. Al final de cada semana su niño(a) llevará el cuadernillo a la casa. Lea la historieta a su niño(a) o leánla en voz alta juntos, señalando cada palabra al decirla. Leer varias veces ayudará a su niño(a) a practicar las destrezas de la lección.

Practicando con el Take-Home Book

Pida a su niño(a) señalar en la historieta palabras que incluyan el sonido de la vocal o de la consonante para esa lección. Luego pídale que resuma la historieta en una frase. Escriba lo que dice su niño(a) y después lean juntos lo que escribió.

Lesson Skills and Take-Home Books

Lesson 26 **Zz:** "Zig, Zag, Buzz!"
Lesson 27 **Short Vowel Review:** "Lots of Fun"
Lesson 28 **Single Letter Long Vowels e, i, o:** "We Play"
Lesson 29 **Final e (a_e):** "The Hat"
Lesson 30 **Final e (o_e, i_e):** "The Bike Ride"

Ampliando el aprendizaje

Con su niño(a) busque palabras con vocales con sonido largo en libros, letreros, portadas de revistas, etc. Haga una libreta con palabras que descubran juntos.

Rete a su niño(a) a identificar, ya sea en su casa o en otros lugares, objetos que tengan vocales con sonido largo. Por ejemplo: "I spy a bike."

 Visite SadlierConnect.com **para recursos para el estudiante y la familia.**

Learn and Blend

Directions: Listen and join in.

Z…z…z…
Zip that zipper
up and down.

Zz

Blend It

Directions: Chorally say the sounds and read the words.

INTRODUCE

1. z	y	qu	j
2. zip	rip	zap	tap
3. buzz	fizz	mess	puff

REVIEW

4. yes	quit	jam	fun

CHALLENGE

5. lip	slip	sell	smell

IN CONTEXT

6. What can buzz?

7. Zip it up.

Daily Practice

Directions: Do one activity each day. Then check the box.

☐ Build Fluency Read the words each day by yourself and to a partner.

☐ Mark It Circle all the words with z.

☐ Spell It Have a partner say each word. Write the word. Check your answer.

☐ Write About It Use the words to create a story. Draw a box around words from the list that you used.

Read-Spell-Write

Directions: Write each word two times. Say each letter as you write it.

1. for _____

2. finds _____

Use in Context

Directions: Complete each sentence with a word from above.
Read the finished sentences to a partner.

1. I will look _____ it.

2. Ned _____ a red rock.

1

Name _____

Zig, Zag, Buzz!

— Fold —

The bee looks for a flower.
Zig, zag. Zip!

— Fold —

The bee looks for a friend.
Zig, zag. Zip!

4

2

The bee finds a flower.
Zip, zap, buzz!

The bee likes the flower.
Buzz, buzz, buzz.

3

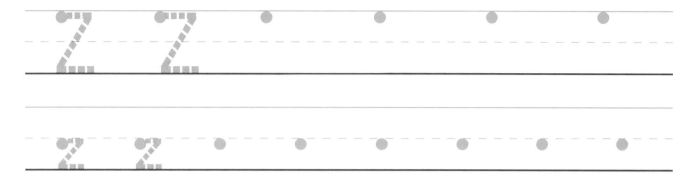

Trace and Write

Directions: Trace and write the letters **Z** and **z**. These letters stand for /z/. Say the sound each time you write the letter.

Directions: Say the name of the picture. Write **Zz** on the line if the picture name begins with the /z/ sound.

1. _____

2. _____

3. _____

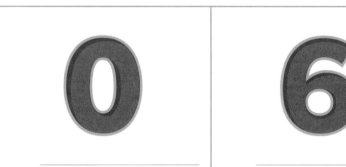

4. _____

5. _____

6. _____

Think and Write

Directions: Listen to each picture name. Write the first letter of the picture name on the line.

1.  _____

2.  _____

Directions: Listen to each picture name. Write the letter for each sound in a separate box.

3.

4.

Listen and Spell

Directions: Write each word and sentence that you hear.

1. _____

2. _____

Trace, Write, and Build

Directions: Trace and write each word.
Then build each word with letter cards.

TRACE	WRITE
for	
finds	
zip	
rip	
fuzz	

Sort It Out

Directions: Look at the pictures on page 397. Say each picture name. Then sort the pictures by beginning sound.

Ss	Zz

What words do you know with these sounds?

_____

- -

_____

- -

_____

Read and Write

Directions: Say the picture name. Circle the first letter of the picture name. Write the letter on the line.

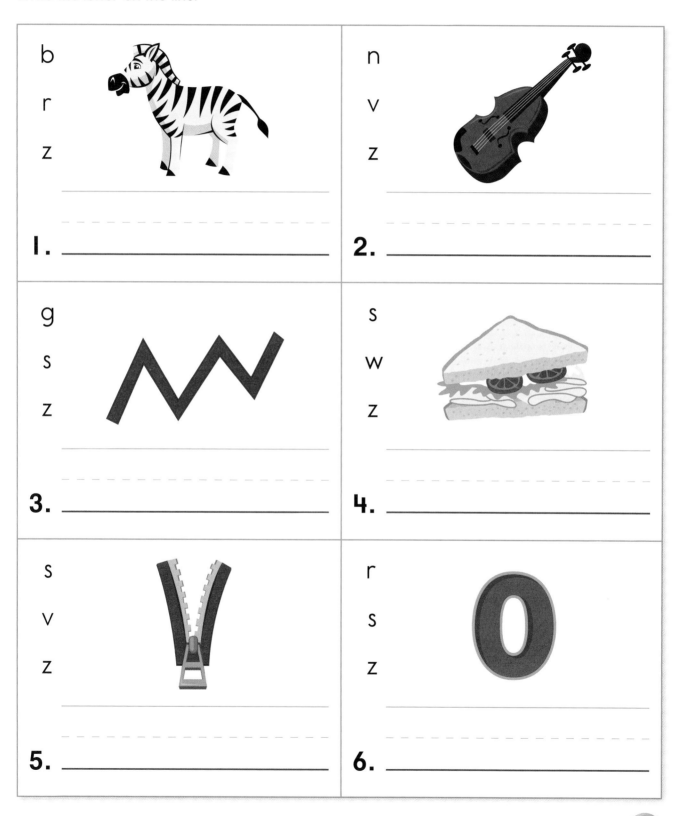

b
r
z

1. _____

n
v
z

2. _____

g
s
z

3. _____

s
w
z

4. _____

s
v
z

5. _____

r
s
z

6. _____

Build Fluency

Directions: Complete each sentence with a word from the box.

for   read

1. Is that box _____ me?

2. Kim can _____ well.

Directions: Write a sentence using each word.

3. | yell | _____

_____

4. | zip | _____

_____

Write About It

Directions: Read "Zig, Zag, Buzz!" again. Draw a picture about bees. Write about your picture.

Fluency Check

Directions: Listen to the child read the list below. Mark one check in the green box if the word is read correctly (accuracy). Mark another check in the blue box if it is read automatically (fluency).

CUMULATIVE ASSESSMENT							
Lesson	**Word**			**Lesson**	**Word**		
26	zip	☐	☐	**23**	jugs	☐	☐
	zap	☐	☐		jog	☐	☐
	buzz	☐	☐		jet	☐	☐
	slip	☐	☐		jam	☐	☐
25	yes	☐	☐	**22**	fun	☐	☐
	yell	☐	☐		rub	☐	☐
	yum	☐	☐		duck	☐	☐
	yap	☐	☐		bus	☐	☐
24	quit	☐	☐	**21**	van	☐	☐
	quick	☐	☐		vet	☐	☐
	kicks	☐	☐		top	☐	☐
	kit	☐	☐		stop	☐	☐

Number Correct (accuracy): _____ /24

Number Automatic (fluency): _____ /24

Learn and Blend

Directions: Listen and join in.

A as in cat. E as in hen.
I as in fish. O as in ox.
U as in duck.
We see lots of animals.
What luck!

Short Vowels

a e i o u

Blend It

Directions: Chorally say the sounds and read the words.

INTRODUCE

1. e	i	o	u
2. pack	mess	hug	bells
3. bugs	mom	sad	bed

REVIEW

4. pig	fox	ran	sock

CHALLENGE

5. vans	digs	boxes	buses

IN CONTEXT

6. Kim likes to run.

7. Ed has a big dog.

Daily Practice

Directions: Do one activity each day. Then check the box.

☐ **Build Fluency** Read the words each day by yourself and to a partner.

☐ **Mark It** Circle all the words with short a. Underline all the words with short o.

☐ **Spell It** Have a partner say each word. Write the word. Check your answer.

☐ **Write About It** Use the words to create a story. Draw a box around words from the list that you used.

Read-Spell-Write

Directions: Write each word two times. Say each letter as you write it.

1. was _____

2. too _____

Use in Context

Directions: Complete each sentence with a word from above.
Read the finished sentences to a partner.

1. Max _____ sick.

2. It is _____ wet to go out.

Name _____

Lots of Fun

"I went on a swing," said Jill.

"It was lots of fun!"

1

"Was it this one?" said Liz.

"I like this book, too."

4

2

"I ran up a big hill," said Liz.
"It was lots of fun, too."

"I got a book," said Jill.
"It was a cat book."

3

Write

Directions: Write each sentence. Use your best handwriting.

1. The cat sits.

2. A fox can run.

3. I see a red rug.

Directions: Write your own sentence. Use the words will and mop.

4.

Think and Write

Directions: Listen to each picture name. Write the first letter or letters of the picture name on the line.

1.  _____

2.  _____

Directions: Listen to each picture name. Write the letter for each sound in a separate box.

3.

4.

Listen and Spell

Directions: Write each word and sentence that you hear.

1. _____

2. _____

Trace, Write, and Build

Directions: Trace and write each word.
Then build each word with letter cards.

TRACE	WRITE
was	
too	
bus	
mom	
bed	

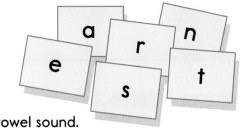

Sort It Out

Directions: Read each word. Then sort the words by their vowel sound.
Write each word in the correct box.

bit	bug	cat	hot	leg
map	pen	pot	tip	tub

Short a	
Short e	
Short i	
Short o	
Short u	

What other words do you know with these short vowel sounds?

_____

_____

_____

Read and Write

Directions: Say the picture name. Circle the word for the picture.
Write it on the line.

pan
pen
ten

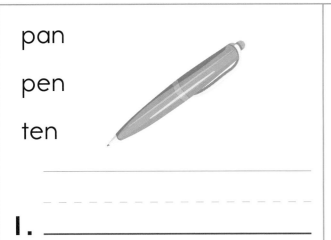

1. _____

bug
bun
bus

2. _____

rug
run
sun

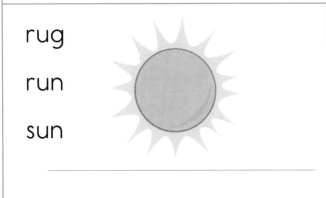

3. _____

fan
fin
pin

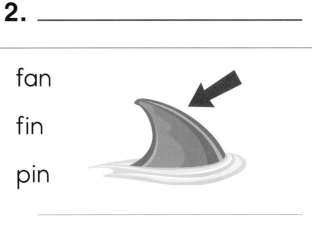

4. _____

leg
lock
log

5. _____

bag
bat
tag

6. _____

Build Fluency

Directions: Complete each sentence with a word from the box.

finds	was

1. Sam _____ the cat.

2. Ed _____ sad.

Directions: Write a sentence using each word.

3. buzz _____

_____

4. hop _____

_____

Write About It

Directions: Read "Lots of Fun" again. Draw a picture about Jill or Liz. Write about your picture.

Fluency Check

Directions: Listen to the child read the list below. Mark one check in the green box if the word is read correctly (accuracy). Mark another check in the blue box if it is read automatically (fluency).

CUMULATIVE ASSESSMENT						
Lesson	Word			Lesson	Word	
27	pack	☐ ☐		**24**	quit	☐ ☐
	mess	☐ ☐			quick	☐ ☐
	hug	☐ ☐			kicks	☐ ☐
	bills	☐ ☐			kit	☐ ☐
26	zip	☐ ☐		**23**	jugs	☐ ☐
	zap	☐ ☐			jog	☐ ☐
	buzz	☐ ☐			jet	☐ ☐
	slip	☐ ☐			jam	☐ ☐
25	yes	☐ ☐		**22**	fun	☐ ☐
	yell	☐ ☐			rub	☐ ☐
	yum	☐ ☐			duck	☐ ☐
	yap	☐ ☐			bus	☐ ☐

Number Correct (accuracy): _____ / 24

Number Automatic (fluency): _____ / 24

Learn and Blend

Directions: Listen and join in.

E as in me.
I as in hi.
O as in go, so,
and no.

Long
Vowels
e i o

Blend It

Directions: Chorally read the words.

INTRODUCE

1. me   he   we   she

2. no   go   so   hi

REVIEW

3. go   got   hi   hit

4. me   met   we   wet

CHALLENGE

5. lap   clap   lock   block

IN CONTEXT

6. We go to school.

7. He is so fun!

Daily Practice

Directions: Do one activity each day. Then check the box.

☐ Build Fluency Read the words each day by yourself and to a partner.

☐ Mark It Circle all the words that end in long e. Underline all the words that end in long o.

☐ Spell It Have a partner say each word. Write the word. Check your answer.

☐ Write About It Use the words to create a story. Draw a box around words from the list that you used.

Read-Spell-Write

Directions: Write each word two times. Say each letter as you write it.

1. come _____

_____

2. some _____

Use in Context

Directions: Complete each sentence with a word from above.
Read the finished sentences to a partner.

1. _____ with me.

2. We will have _____ fun.

Name

We Play

Fold

Dan will come to my house.
We will go to the park.

1

Farm Fresh

Dan stops.
He sees a van.
We can get some food. Yum!

4

2

We see Pat.
"Hi!" we yell.
"Come with us!"

3

We run and play.
We have lots of fun.

Write

Directions: Write each sentence. Use your best handwriting.

1. We can help.

2. Hi! I am Max.

3. Ben is so sad.

Directions: Write your own sentence. Use the words he and go.

4.

Think and Write

Directions: Listen to each word. Write the letter for each sound in a separate box. Then write the word on the line.

1.

2.

3.

Listen and Spell

Directions: Write each word and sentence that you hear.

1.

2.

Trace, Write, and Build

Directions: Trace and write each word.
Then build each word with letter cards.

TRACE	WRITE
come	
some	
me	
bed	
no	
hi	

Sort It Out

Directions: Read each word. Then sort the words.
Write each word in the correct box.

| hi | him | me | men | no |
| not | so | sock | we | web |

Long Vowel Sound	Short Vowel Sound

What did you notice about the vowels and
vowel sounds in each box?

_____

_____

_____

Read and Write

Directions: Read each word. Circle the word that has the long vowel sound. Write it on the line.

be bed beg 1. _____	hi him hit 2. _____
get go got 3. _____	wag we wet 4. _____
he hen hot 5. _____	net no nut 6. _____

Build Fluency

Directions: Complete each sentence with a word from the box.

too   some

1. That pot is _____ hot.

2. Can I have _____ jam?

Directions: Write a sentence using each word.

3. | go | _____

4. | run | _____

Write About It

Directions: Read "We Play" again. Draw a picture that shows what the kids do. Write about your picture.

Fluency Check

Directions: Listen to the child read the list below. Mark one check in the green box if the word is read correctly (accuracy). Mark another check in the blue box if it is read automatically (fluency).

CUMULATIVE ASSESSMENT							
Lesson	**Word**			**Lesson**	**Word**		
28	me	☐	☐	**25**	yes	☐	☐
	go	☐	☐		yell	☐	☐
	hi	☐	☐		yum	☐	☐
	no	☐	☐		yap	☐	☐
27	pack	☐	☐	**24**	quit	☐	☐
	mess	☐	☐		quick	☐	☐
	hug	☐	☐		kicks	☐	☐
	bills	☐	☐		kit	☐	☐
26	zip	☐	☐	**23**	jugs	☐	☐
	zap	☐	☐		jog	☐	☐
	buzz	☐	☐		jet	☐	☐
	slip	☐	☐		jam	☐	☐

Number Correct (accuracy): _____ /24

Number Automatic (fluency): _____ /24

Learn and Blend

Directions: Listen and join in.

A as in grape.
I ate a plate
of grapes.

Final e
a_e

Blend It

Directions: Chorally read the words.

INTRODUCE

1. mad	made	tap	tape
2. bake	cake	take	lake
3. gave	save	same	game

REVIEW

4. no	we	quick	zap

CHALLENGE

5. make	makes	take	takes

IN CONTEXT

6. I made a big cake.

7. We take the same bus to school.

Daily Practice

Directions: Do one activity each day. Then check the box.

☐ Build Fluency Read the words each day by yourself and to a partner.

☐ Mark It Circle all the words with long a.

☐ Spell It Have a partner say each word. Write the word. Check your answer.

☐ Write About It Use the words to create a story. Draw a box around words from the list that you used.

Read-Spell-Write

Directions: Write each word two times. Say each letter as you write it.

1. your _____

2. very _____

Use in Context

Directions: Complete each sentence with a word from above.
Read the finished sentences to a partner.

1. That is _____ hat.

2. Jan ran _____ fast.

Name _____

The Hat

1

Do you hate my hat?

No. I like your hat!

Yes, I did!

We can have some.

It is very good!

4

2

Your hat is very big.
It is! I made it.

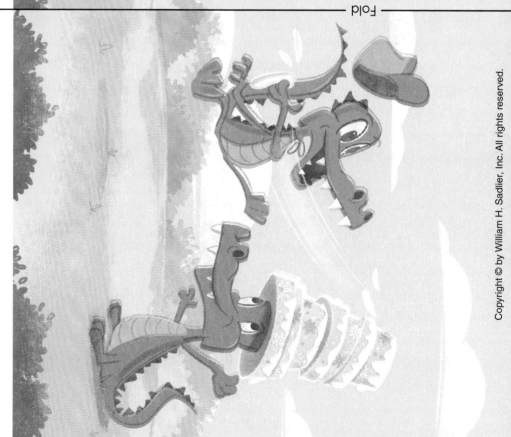

That is a cake hat!
Did you bake it?

3

Write

Directions: Write each sentence. Use your best handwriting.

1. Jake wins the game.

2. Al finds a rake.

3. We will be late.

Directions: Write your own sentence. Use the words bake and cake.

4.

Think and Write

Directions: Listen to each picture name. Trace the **silent e**. Then write the letter for each sound in a separate box.

1.

2.

Listen and Spell

Directions: Write each word and sentence that you hear.

1. _____

2. _____

Trace, Write, and Build

Directions: Trace and write each word.
Then build each word with letter cards.

TRACE	WRITE
your	
very	
rake	
take	
gave	

Sort It Out

Directions: Read each word. Then sort the words.
Write each word in the correct box.

| at | ate | cap | cape | hat |
| hate | mad | made | tap | tape |

a

a_e

What did you notice about the words that
have an **e** at the end?

_____

- -

_____

- -

_____

Read and Write

Directions: Read each word. Circle the word that has the long vowel sound.
Write it on the line.

cake can kick 	rag rake rock
1. _____	**2.** _____
tack tap tape	wag wave wax
3. _____	**4.** _____
cat gap gate 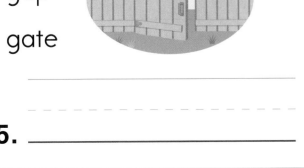	back lake lock 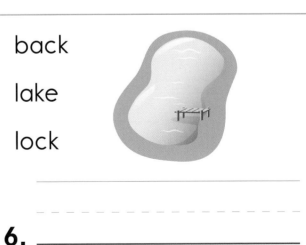
5. _____	**6.** _____

Build Fluency

Directions: Complete each sentence with a word from the box.

come	your

1. Jen will _____, too.

2. Is that _____ tan cat?

Directions: Write a sentence using each word.

3. | make | _____

_____

_____

4. | He | _____

_____

_____

Write About It

Directions: Read "The Hat" again. Draw a picture about the hat.
Write about your picture.

Fluency Check

Directions: Listen to the child read the list below. Mark one check in the green box if the word is read correctly (accuracy). Mark another check in the blue box if it is read automatically (fluency).

CUMULATIVE ASSESSMENT								
Lesson	Word			Lesson	Word		
29	bake	☐	☐	**26**	zip	☐	☐
	save	☐	☐		zap	☐	☐
	mad	☐	☐		buzz	☐	☐
	made	☐	☐		slip	☐	☐
28	me	☐	☐	**25**	yes	☐	☐
	go	☐	☐		yell	☐	☐
	hi	☐	☐		yum	☐	☐
	no	☐	☐		yap	☐	☐
27	pack	☐	☐	**24**	quit	☐	☐
	mess	☐	☐		quick	☐	☐
	hug	☐	☐		kicks	☐	☐
	bills	☐	☐		kit	☐	☐

Number Correct (accuracy): _____ /24

Number Automatic (fluency): _____ /24

Learn and Blend

Directions: Listen and join in.

O as in home.
I as in mice.
A hole is a nice home
for mice!

Final e
o_e i_e

Blend It

Directions: Chorally read the words.

INTRODUCE

1. hop	hope	rid	ride
2. bike	like	side	wide
3. home	bone	five	hide

REVIEW

4. take	name	smile	so

CHALLENGE

5. hope	hoping	ride	riding

IN CONTEXT

6. I hope I can go.

7. I like to ride the bike.

Daily Practice

Directions: Do one activity each day. Then check the box.

☐ Build Fluency Read the words each day by yourself and to a partner.

☐ Mark It Circle all the words with long o. Underline the words with long i.

☐ Spell It Have a partner say each word. Write the word. Check your answer.

☐ Write About It Use the words to create a story. Draw a box around words from the list that you used.

Read-Spell-Write

Directions: Write each word two times. Say each letter as you write it.

1. use _____

2. blue _____

Use in Context

Directions: Complete each sentence with a word from above.
Read the finished sentences to a partner.

1. Where is my _____ sock?

2. We will _____ the map.

Name _____

The Bike Ride

— Fold —

1

Mike will go on a big
bike ride.
Hope will go, too.

— Fold —

The sun sets.
The park will close.
It is time to ride home.

4

2

Mike will use the red bike.

Hope will use the blue bike.

They hop on the bikes.

They like to ride.

Up, up, and down.

3

Write

Directions: Write each sentence. Use your best handwriting.

1. She is nine.

2. The man has a rope.

3. My kite is at home.

Directions: Write your own sentence. Use the words like and joke.

4.

Think and Write

Directions: Listen to each picture name. Trace the **silent e**. Then write the letter for each sound in a separate box.

1.

2.

Listen and Spell

Directions: Write each word and sentence that you hear.

1. _____

2. _____

Word Building

Trace, Write, and Build

Directions: Trace and write each word.
Then build each word with letter cards.

TRACE	WRITE
use	
blue	
bike	
like	
home	

Sort It Out

Directions: Read each word. Then sort the words.
Write each word in the correct box.

| kit | kite | not | note | pin |
| pine | rip | ripe | rob | robe |

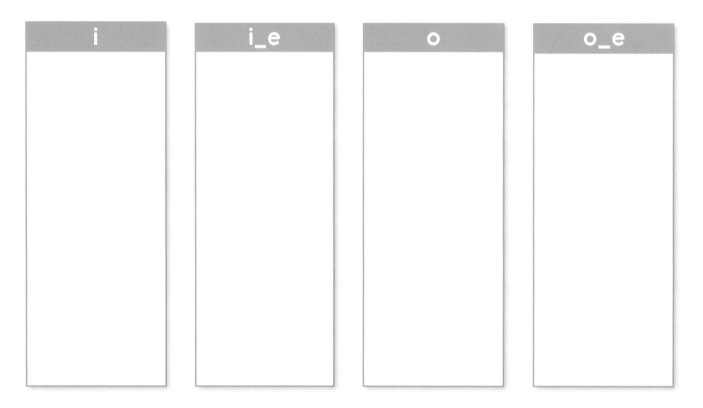

| i | i_e | o | o_e |

What did you notice about the words that
have an **e** at the end?

_____

_____

_____

Read and Write

Directions: Read each word. Circle the word that has the long vowel sound. Write it on the line.

---

fill

five

fix

5

1. _____

---

can

cap

cone

2. _____

---

rob

rope

rug

3. _____

---

cape

kiss

kite

4. _____

---

hole

hop

hot

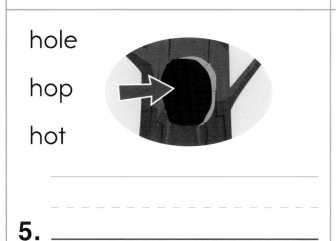

5. _____

---

back

bike

bit

6. _____

Build Fluency

Directions: Complete each sentence with a word from the box.

very	use

1. I _____ a blue pen.

2. The dog bone is _____ big.

Directions: Write a sentence using each word.

3. | ate | _____

_____

4. | ride | _____

_____

Write About It

Directions: Read "The Bike Ride" again. Draw a picture about the bike ride. Write about your picture.

Fluency Check

Directions: Listen to the child read the list below. Mark one check in the green box if the word is read correctly (accuracy). Mark another check in the blue box if it is read automatically (fluency).

CUMULATIVE ASSESSMENT							
Lesson	Word			Lesson	Word		
30	side	☐	☐	**27**	pack	☐	☐
	bike	☐	☐		mess	☐	☐
	hop	☐	☐		hug	☐	☐
	hope	☐	☐		bills	☐	☐
29	bake	☐	☐	**26**	zip	☐	☐
	save	☐	☐		zap	☐	☐
	mad	☐	☐		buzz	☐	☐
	made	☐	☐		slip	☐	☐
28	me	☐	☐	**25**	yes	☐	☐
	go	☐	☐		yell	☐	☐
	hi	☐	☐		yum	☐	☐
	no	☐	☐		yap	☐	☐

Number Correct (accuracy): _____ /24

Number Automatic (fluency): _____ /24

Lesson 5	Lesson 4	Lesson 3	Lesson 2	Lesson 1
	6			
10				
				10

This page intentionally left blank.

Lesson 10   Lesson 9   Lesson 8   Lesson 7   Lesson 6

Picture Cards   389

This page intentionally left blank.

Lesson 15 | Lesson 14 | Lesson 13 | Lesson 12 | Lesson 11

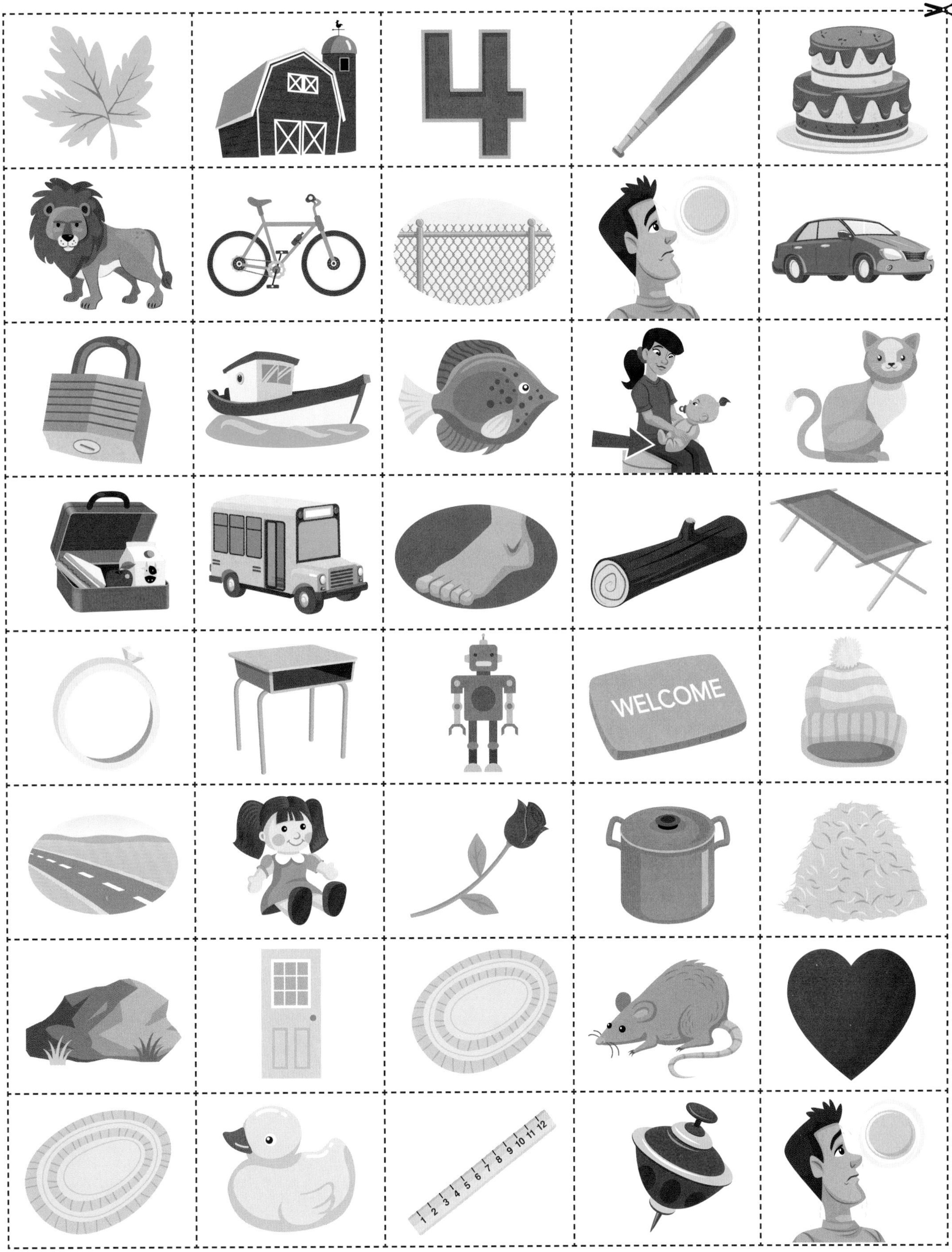

This page intentionally left blank.

Lesson 20	Lesson 19	Lesson 18	Lesson 17	Lesson 16

Lesson 20	Lesson 19	Lesson 18	Lesson 17	Lesson 16

This page intentionally left blank.

Picture Cards **395**

This page intentionally left blank.

Lesson 30	Lesson 29	Lesson 28	Lesson 27	Lesson 26
kit	at	hi	bit	
kite	ate	him	bug	
not	cap	me	cat	
note	cape	men	hot	
pin	hat	no	leg	
pine	hate	not	map	
rip	mad	so	pen	
ripe	made	sock	pot	
rob	tap	we	tip	
robe	tape	web	tub	

| Lesson 30 | Lesson 29 | Lesson 28 | Lesson 27 | Lesson 26 |

This page intentionally left blank.

a	k	u	e
b	l	v	f
c	m	w	g
d	n	x	h
e	o	y	i
f	p	z	j
g	q	a	k
h	r	b	l
i	s	c	m
j	t	d	n

o	y	i	s
p	z	j	t
q	a	k	u
r	b	l	v
s	c	m	w
t	d	n	x
u	e	o	y
v	f	p	z
w	g	q	a
x	h	r	e